D1484735

PRESENTED TO:

_____

FROM:

_____

DATE:

_____

The
Ultimate
Journey

The Ultimate Journey

a novel

JIM STOVALL

EMBASSY BOOKS
www.embassybooks.in

THE ULTIMATE JOURNEY

© 2011 Jim Stovall

Te website addresses recommended throughout this book are offered as a resource to you. Th ese web sites are not intended in any way to be or imply an endorsement on the part of Embassy Books, nor do we vouch for their content.

This story is a work of fiction. All characters and events are the product of the author's imagination. Any resemblance to any person, living or dead, is coincidental.

Th e Team: John Blase, Amy Kiechlin, Jack Campbell, Karen Athen
Cover Design: Sarah Schultz
Cover Photos: iStockphoto 10455657; 4767700; 2616845

First published in India 2011

Published in India by :
EMBASSY BOOK DISTRIBUTORS
120, Great Western Building,
Maharashtra Chamber of Commerce Lane,
Fort, Mumbai - 400 023.
Tel : (+91-22) 22819546 / 32967415
Email : info@embassybooks.in
Website: www.embassybooks.in

ISBN 13: 978-93-80227-94-8

Printed in India by Repro India Ltd., Mumbai

This book is dedicated to Dorothy Thompson
who has, fifteen times, taken my dictated words
and turned them into a manuscript.
It is also dedicated to the wonderful team
at David C Cook who has, once again,
taken my manuscript and turned it into a book.
And, finally, this book is dedicated
to Rick Eldridge
who, as executive producer, has twice
before taken these characters
and brought their story to the silver screen
in *The Ultimate Gift* and *The Ultimate Life*.

I wonder if my life had been
Of some completely different vein
Would I have scaled more lofty heights,
Waved more banners, flashed more lights,
And pressed my head where royalty has lain?

Or what if I asked but to see
Exquisite beauty, just for me?
Would I have ever dared to look
Beyond the diary or the book
That held the secrets wise men left
For such as we, for such as we?

From the personal diary of Joye Kanelakos

INTRODUCTION

Preparing for the Journey

My dear readers, you and I are preparing to take a journey in time and space, between the covers of this book, with some very special characters. Some of you will be traveling this way for the first time while others have twice before gone on this quest in the pages of the previous books, *The Ultimate Gift* and *The Ultimate Life,* as well as the two movies of the same name from 20th Century Fox.

One of my late great movie partners, Scott Fithian, was fond of saying, "If you can tell a great story, you earn the right to share your message." In this book, I will endeavor mightily to both tell a good story and share a powerful message.

The characters in this book have lived with me now for over a decade. They have become the basis for books, movies, workbooks, public school and college courses, corporate training, religious study, songs, poems, and so much more. I hope you will greet them as you would an old friend and embrace what they have to share with you.

In the final analysis, it's really not about their gift, their life, or their journey. It's about you and me and where we are going.

I have had the privilege of sharing my message with millions of people around the world through books, movies, columns, television, and speeches. On every occasion, I extend an offer that I now want to present to you. Anytime you need encouragement, direction, or simply someone to listen to your hopes and dreams, you can call me at 918-627-1000 or send me an email at Jim@JimStovall.com.

I want you to know and understand that I am serious about your success, and I don't want to be just another guy who sells you a book, a movie, or whose speech you sit through. I want to be your partner in success and be your cheerleader as you find and fulfill your destiny.

I am not someone who has mastered everything in these pages. I will never claim to be the voice of experience or expertise. I do not have all the answers. I only hope to frame the questions so you and I can explore the possibilities.

Like most everyone, I have not yet arrived at the place where I want to be, but I am proud, pleased, and excited to join you on this Ultimate Journey.

Jim Stovall

Table of Contents

The journey of life
is a matter of traveling well
rather than reaching a destination.

ONE

The Ultimate Life

It was one of those miraculous, magical days that are destined to fondly dwell in one's memories for years to come. I had just parallel parked on the first pass. This may not seem noteworthy unless or until one realizes that the car I parked is a vintage super-stretch limousine that is more valuable than my house.

I have driven this automotive masterpiece for the Stevens family for well over two decades. I began my service working for Howard "Red" Stevens when both the limousine and I were much newer.

My name is James—Jim to my friends and everyone else when I'm not wearing this chauffeur's uniform.

Red Stevens was a legendary figure who was truly larger than life in every way. He earned, spent, and gave away billions of dollars throughout his life. His successes and his shortcomings were all monumental and could be measured on a grand scale. No history of business or industry in the twentieth century could be complete without including the exploits of Red Stevens.

Late in his life he realized his success, fame, and wealth had taken a toll on his entire family. While Mr. Stevens had been out changing the world, he had failed to have a similar impact on his own family.

Then there was that fateful day when the best doctors and medical experts around the world informed Mr. Stevens that his days on this earth were very limited. News like that would cause anyone to reevaluate their life and make some changes. Mr. Stevens reevaluated his priorities and changed his life the same way he did everything—in a big way.

When you drive someone everywhere they go and talk with them constantly, you get to know them in a rare and special way.

Although we never crossed that invisible employer-employee boundary, I believe I'm safe in saying Red Stevens and I were friends.

After Mr. Stevens had completed all the medical tests, gotten second and third opinions, and verified the bad news, he reacted in that decisive manner I had come to know and love. I will never forget that unwavering voice booming from the back of the limousine.

"James, I've seen my last doctor on this thing, and the verdict is in."

I heard a deep sigh as he continued more reflectively. "I always knew I wasn't going to live forever, so it's time to make some plans and set some things straight. I never thought much about dying, but there's got to be a right way to do it."

He realized that the wealth and power that had been a tool for him to reshape the world around him had been the downfall of his children and grandchildren. Riches inspired Red Stevens to be more and do more. It caused his family to be less and do nothing.

As I pulled away from the medical center, I heard him say, "James, let's go see Ted Hamilton."

Mr. Hamilton was to the world of law what Red Stevens had been to the world of business. They had been partners, colleagues, and special friends since the beginning.

As I pulled up in front of the marble high-rise building that housed the law offices of Hamilton, Hamilton, and Hamilton, as usual Mr. Hamilton was waiting on the sidewalk in front of the building. I was never quite sure how he always knew we were coming, but he never failed to greet Red Stevens as I held open the back door of the limousine.

The two men hugged and walked toward the building.

People today would simply look upon these two giants as well-dressed, energetic men in their mideighties, but when they first got together over sixty years ago, the thought of a white man and a black man as friends and confidants was unthinkable.

Red Stevens and Mr. Hamilton had shrugged off the absurdity of racism then, just like they had surmounted every obstacle that had confronted them throughout the years.

After much contemplation and with Mr. Hamilton's counsel, Red Stevens determined that he would leave his fortune and legacy to his grandson Jason Stevens in the form of a bequest that came to be known around the world as The Ultimate Gift.

Instead of making Jason Stevens an instant billionaire, Red decided to teach Jason the lessons that Red had learned over a lifetime by sending him on a twelve-month odyssey that was monitored and orchestrated by Mr. Hamilton.

Red Stevens set aside his long-standing distaste of being on camera and sat down long enough to make videos on a number of life lessons to be shared with his grandson at the appropriate time.

After Red's death and a yearlong struggle, Jason emerged controlling billions of dollars and, more importantly, he had internalized the best parts of his grandfather.

Jason set out to continue and build upon the philanthropic work his grandfather had done throughout his life. In this way, he became his grandfather's living legacy.

Red Stevens' children and other grandchildren not only failed to receive the bulk of his estate, but they also never learned the life lessons that Red left Jason through The Ultimate Gift quest.

Red had left various companies, properties, and managed trusts to support the rest of his family, but their greed and bitterness resulted in a lawsuit aimed at Jason and the billions of dollars he controlled for the charitable foundation. A bitter court battle ensued, but thanks to Mr. Hamilton's expertise, a judge's wisdom, and Red Stevens' shrewd planning, Jason emerged victorious with the charitable trust intact, and much of the damage from the family's anger, greed, and bitterness healed.

Either as a part of Red Stevens' will or through the odyssey of The Ultimate Gift, Jason somehow inherited the limousine and me. I became his driver and constant companion as, month after month, he pursued the gifts of work, money, family, love, and the other components that made up the twelve aspects of Red Stevens' Ultimate Gift to him.

Jason was transformed into a new man throughout that year, and I will admit to being greatly changed myself.

During that process, Jason met a special young lady named Alexia and her nine-year-old daughter, Emily. Emily was struggling with leukemia, and the disease eventually took her life, but I am proud to say it never took her joy, her laughter, or her dignity.

Emily's death left a void in everyone who knew her but somehow drew Jason and Alexia together. Emily will never be forgotten, and her impact remains in everyone whose life she touched.

That day, we had gathered at a very special place known as Emily's Home. It had been funded by the Red Stevens Foundation and had been the focal point of the Stevens family legal battle that had recently been resolved. Emily's Home is a home for families of children suffering with serious illnesses. It allows the family to stay together and be close as their child receives treatment at the nearby medical center.

That special place, which is usually a refuge for families dealing with pain and suffering, had been turned into the ornate and joyous setting for Jason and Alexia's wedding. The fires of pain that had come from Emily's death had forged a bond between Jason and Alexia that could never be broken.

The limousine had gotten an extra coat of wax, and my chauffeur's uniform had received an extra cleaning and pressing for the occasion. The ceremony was conducted by Judge Neely, who had presided over the recent legal civil war in the Stevens family after the initial judge had retired. The wedding went off without a hitch, and as the couple was presented as Mr. and Mrs. Jason Stevens, thousands of butterflies were released in memory of Emily and the joy and beauty she brought into the world.

Friends, relatives, associates, and the obligatory media each had to have their moments with the newlyweds. Finally, Jason and Alexia made their way to the limousine, where I was on duty holding open the back door in the prescribed manner.

Normally, limousine drivers don't speak unless they're spoken to, but on that day, I proclaimed, "My hearty congratulations, Mr. and Mrs. Stevens."

Jason smiled and said, "Thank you, James, but I've always told you to call me Jason, and from now on, you can simply call my bride Alexia."

"Thank you, Mr. Stevens," I replied formally.

Some habits die hard.

I helped the couple settle into the backseat of the car, careful not to damage Mrs. Stevens' wedding gown. Just when all was in order, and I was preparing to close the door, I heard the unmistakable voice of Mr. Hamilton as he approached.

"Just one moment, James, if I may."

Mr. Hamilton has a way of asking questions as if there is no choice or option regarding your response. This is probably part of what has made him one of the world's greatest lawyers.

I stepped back to allow Mr. Hamilton to approach the newlyweds in the backseat. I stood beside Mr. Hamilton's longtime assistant, Miss Hastings. She has the capacity to seem like royalty and a servant at the same time.

Mr. Hamilton leaned into the backseat of the limousine. He shook Jason's hand warmly and kissed Alexia on the cheek. Then he handed them a package, explaining, "He had one last gift he wanted me to give you as a wedding present."

Jason began to blurt out a question, "Who …? What …?"

Hamilton merely backed away, turned toward me, and shook my hand, saying, "James, I know this Mr. Stevens will appreciate your help and friendship as much as the last one did."

As I basked in the glow of his words and Jason continued to stammer out questions, Mr. Hamilton strode away with dignity, accompanied by the ever-present Miss Hastings.

Closing the back door of the limousine and making my way around the vehicle to the driver's compartment, I realized that the transition was complete. One era had ended while another began. As we are going through a circumstance in life, rarely does the transition seem apparent, but when we look back on events with the benefit of hindsight, it is clear that a single moment in time brought about the change.

Thanks to Red Stevens' immense wealth and private jet, Jason had been all around the world. He had vacationed in the most exclusive resorts and visited many rare and special places. But for their honeymoon, the couple had decided to spend a week at a private beach house just a few hours' drive away.

I inserted my key in the ignition and started the massive custom limousine engine. I glanced in the rearview mirror for the customary signal from Mr. Stevens to proceed, but he and his new bride were simply staring at the mysterious package from Red Stevens that Mr. Hamilton had delivered.

One of the many lessons I had learned from my years with Jason's grandfather is that every day is a gift, because we never know what the package holds.

The journey of life is a gift
we have been given.

Our lives should be lived as
gifts to those who follow.

TWO

The Ultimate Gift

The three of us were frozen in time and space within the cocoon of the plush stretch limousine. I sat behind the wheel, afraid to talk or even move as I realized this was a monumental occasion. I didn't know what Red Stevens had put inside the wrapped package that Mr. Hamilton had delivered, but I knew it had to be extraordinary.

As I looked on in the rearview mirror, Jason and Alexia continued to stare with furrowed brows at the wrapped package that Jason held in his lap. Finally, they glanced at each other. Jason shrugged, took a deep breath, and tore open the package.

As Alexia set aside the wrapping paper, an ordinary cardboard box was revealed. Jason slowly opened the lid and peered inside. He chuckled as he reached in and pulled out a DVD.

He said, "I thought I had seen the last of his video lectures."

Although the box held more, Jason simply couldn't wait to hear from his grandfather one more time, so he slid the DVD into the player in the back of the limousine.

We all held our breath in anticipation, and after several seconds of static, Red Stevens appeared on the several flat screens that had been installed throughout the limousine.

I stared at the late, great Red Stevens on the small screen in the dashboard. He had been my boss and my friend for many years. I still couldn't believe that someone filled with so much life and energy could really be gone.

Even though he was terminally ill and closer to ninety years old than eighty, he had a power and vitality that few men ever possess.

He calmly spoke is if he were in the vehicle with us. "My congratulations to the new Mr. and Mrs. Stevens."

A lump formed in my throat as I heard him say, "My greetings and gratitude go out to you, James, for being with me at every important step of my life and for carrying on in the same manner for Jason and his new bride."

I quickly wiped away a tear and glanced in the mirror in time to see Jason and Alexia smiling as they looked in my direction.

Red continued speaking. "I know you're watching this shortly after your wedding ceremony because there was never anyone more reliable than my old friend Ted Hamilton. I can rest peacefully knowing that Miss Hastings will always be there to take care of him."

Red paused for a moment, seeming to collect his thoughts, then continued. "Jason, I bet you thought you were done suffering through my little video lectures."

Jason stared at the screen openmouthed as his grandfather always seemed to know what he was thinking and be one step ahead of him.

Red explained, "Well, this time it's a little different. In the twelve lessons of The Ultimate Gift, I shared with you my thoughts. As you and your wife embark on your new life together, I want to share my experience and myself with you.

"To my new granddaughter-in-law, I would like to say, 'Welcome to the family,' and I hope you know you have my love and respect. You probably already know that my grandson, Jason, is one of the most stubborn, obstinate, and frustrating creatures the good Lord ever made. He's also one of the most giving, loving, and creative people you will ever meet. I am proud of the man he has become, and I am proud that he will build upon the work I started.

"My sainted wife, Hannah, put up with me and gave me her love for more than half a century. She had the amazing ability to look upon me the way she saw her garden. Every year when winter was finally over, she would walk out in that barren plot of ground and just stand there for a while, looking at it. Somehow, Hannah could see what it was and what it could be at the same time. I hope you can do the same with my grandson."

A tear rolled down Alexia's cheek, and she nodded toward the flat-screen television as if Red Stevens were actually sitting there.

Red seemed to speak directly to Alexia. "Young lady, I found out that all we need in this world to be happy are three things: someone to love, something to do, and something to look forward to. For better or for worse, my grandson will keep you supplied with all three for the rest of your life."

Jason and Alexia looked at each other and smiled as Red seemed to shift gears and then continue.

"Outside of Hannah, Ted Hamilton, and James there, I doubt if anyone else knew that I kept a diary throughout my life. There's something about writing things down that makes you look at them differently and think about them in a new way.

"When my doctors told me that I only had a few months left, I started going through all the diaries I had written over the years. In reviewing the various days of my life, I got to relive the high points and the low points of an amazing journey.

"Jason, somehow, I knew you would get through all the tests and the lessons that made up The Ultimate Gift, and when I considered the day you would be starting a new life with your bride, I thought about sharing pieces of myself with you through my diary.

"I've always believed that we need to seek advice and counsel from people who have the things we want. People wanting to tell you how to live your life are a dime a dozen. You can't turn on a TV, a radio, or open a newspaper without some self-proclaimed expert telling you what you ought to be doing, buying, or thinking.

"What I'm talking about is finding people who have been on the journey you are starting and finding out what they did when they were in the place where you are starting today. Even the most well-meaning successful people can slip into the bad habit of telling you what they think you ought to do instead of sharing what they did when they started out."

Red Stevens sighed and seemed to consider his next statement before he spoke.

"Jason, you know I had my successes, and I had my failures. They were all big. I never believed in doing anything halfway, so when I made mistakes, they were obvious to everyone and hurt a lot of people. I'm hoping you will find some wisdom you can take with you in both my victories as well as my defeats.

"I won't bore you with the mundane, normal days, as your life will be filled with enough of those without the burden of reviewing mine; but there were certain days, times, and thoughts I have enjoyed reliving through my diary here in my last days, and I wanted to share them with you as my wedding present."

Jason leaned forward and removed some tissue paper that covered a battered and worn leather book. He took the book out of the box slowly and held it reverently.

Red's voice continued. "Inside that book are the days of my life that made me who I became. I don't share them with you so you can aim at who I was, but, instead, I would like you to learn from my successes and mistakes as you become who you are intended to be. I have a feeling that will be a whole lot more than Howard 'Red' Stevens ever became.

"I've enjoyed reliving parts of my life through those pages, and I hope you will too. You're going to meet some people you already know at a different time and place. You know people like Ted Hamilton and Gus Caldwell as great men now. As I reread about the early days we spent together, I was reminded—as you will learn—that they were great men then, too.

"Any life can only be judged against the backdrop of the time and place in which it is lived out. The Great Depression, World War II, and all the years since have been exciting times. People my age are often referred to as the Greatest Generation. If that is true, it is only because we had great problems and challenges.

"I hope you will find something in my past that will help you in your future."

Jason slowly opened the cover of the book to reveal stained yellow pages filled with that precise, powerful handwriting of his grandfather's that he could never mistake.

Red cleared his throat and proclaimed, "Mr. and Mrs. Stevens, I wish you health, happiness, and everything this life has to offer. I wish for you the love and loyalty of good friends; the joy and wonder of new people and places; and the magic of good books, music, and poetry. I hope you have a life filled with incredible highs, followed by reflective low points that will only serve as a springboard to help you reach and appreciate the next mountaintop.

"I hope on your very best day and at your worst possible moment, you will always know and remember that there was one flawed old man named Howard 'Red' Stevens who will always love you."

The video screen faded to black, and we all sat in silence. Somehow, we knew that Red Stevens would be among us all the days of our lives.

Finally, Jason sat up straight and, sounding more like his grandfather than ever before, said, "James, I believe we're ready to get started with this journey."

Work is a journey we undertake for others
that makes us who we are.

THREE

The Journey of Work

The traffic parted as I pulled the limousine out onto the street. Over the years, I've noticed that the sight of a limousine draws people's attention even as it often keeps them out of your way.

I set my course for the private beach house where Jason and Alexia would be enjoying their honeymoon for the next week. I focused on keeping my pace steady, turns gradual, and starts and stops smooth.

All good chauffeurs know and remember that their passengers are a long way behind them, so a turn that may seem normal to me in the driver's seat can be like a carnival ride to those in the back. The only advice Red Stevens ever gave me about driving his limousine was to be sure to never spill his coffee.

I always keep an eye on my passengers in the mirror, but as we motored toward the coast, I found myself glancing back more than usual. Jason and Alexia were staring at the open leather volume between them.

Jason spoke as he thumbed through the diary. "He has it divided up into sections, just like The Ultimate Gift. The first section is about work, and he has included various pages from his diary, representing the days he thought were significant in his work life."

Both Red Stevens and Jason had become famous through the news coverage surrounding The Ultimate Gift portion of Red Stevens' will and the ensuing court battle among the Stevens family.

For each of the twelve gifts Mr. Stevens had created for Jason's yearlong quest called The Ultimate Gift, he had made a video, sharing with his grandson each important lesson. Jason kept DVD copies of those videos in the limo as well as in his home and office.

He put one of Red's DVDs in the player, and Red Stevens was, once again, riding along with us.

"Jason, when I was much younger than you are now, I learned the satisfaction that comes from a simple four-letter word: work. One of the things my wealth has robbed from you and the entire family is the privilege and satisfaction that comes from doing an honest day's work.

"Now, before you go off the deep end and reject everything I'm going to tell you, I want you to realize that work has brought me everything I have and everything that you have. I regret that I have taken from you the joy of knowing that what you have is what you've earned.

"My earliest memories in the swamps of Louisiana are of work— hard, backbreaking labor that as a young man I resented greatly. My parents had too many mouths to feed and not enough food, so if we wanted to eat, we worked. Later, when I was on my own and came to Texas, I realized that hard work had become a habit for me, and it has served as a true joy all the rest of my life.

"Jason, you have enjoyed the best things that this world has to offer. You have been everywhere, seen everything, and done everything. What you don't understand is how much pleasure these things can bring you when you have earned them yourself, when leisure becomes a reward for hard work instead of a way to avoid work."

As I was thinking about all the hard work and late hours Red Stevens had put in throughout the years, I considered how much I had enjoyed working for him and with him. I guess when you like what you do, it really doesn't seem much like work at all.

I could hear Jason explaining to Alexia, "His diary begins talking about work, here, on October 16th, 1937."

Jason let Alexia examine the handwritten diary page, and then he began reading aloud:

I've only been gone from home a few months, but it seems like forever. People have started calling this financial collapse the Great Depression. Maybe it's because not being able to find work is so depressing.

Today, I stood all day along the roadside where the day laborers wait to be picked up for a few hours or a half day of work. Nothing for me again today. It's rough on me, but some of these other guys have families to feed. It's got to be better tomorrow.

We all fell silent thinking about that long-ago time and place. I could feel the desperation that those frustrated workers must have felt. I realized I had been lucky to work for the Stevens family all these years.

Alexia turned to another page and read:

February 11th, 1940.

Finally found steady work on a ranch here in Texas. The work suits me, and I'm pretty good at it. I'm learning the ropes from my new friend, Gus Caldwell. He seems driven and works harder than anyone else. I am committed to keep up with him, which drives him even harder. We may just kill one another before it's all over.

Alexia turned a page excitedly and said, "Here's an entry just two weeks later."

February 25th, 1940.

Gus and I have been riding the perimeter fence and making repairs for the last week. It keeps us out on the range and away from the bunkhouse. Cold camping out this time of year.

Gus and I talked late into the night about owning our own places someday. If it's this good to work for someone else, it must be great to work for yourself on your own place.

I was trying to pay attention to my driving and not eavesdrop on Jason and Alexia's private conversation, but I found it impossible.

Jason flipped through the pages and read:

May 14th, 1943.

The war in Europe rages on. It seems like we are always taking two steps forward and one step back. I get bored delivering supplies to the front and am eager to do something else, but our CO reminds us that all jobs are important, and without supplies, no one can do anything.

It's good to work for one another and everyone back home. Everyone wants to carry their own weight and not let anyone down.

Jason turned one of the weatherworn pages and read:

July 17th, 1948.

It's a great time to be in the oil business in Texas. A lot of good workers returning from the service and looking for jobs. I've got to bring in one of these wells fast so I can keep everyone on the payroll. These are good men, and they have families to feed.

I heard Gus Caldwell brought in a gusher on his ranch over in the next county. It's only a matter of time.

Jason continued, "And here's his entry two days later."

July 19th, 1948.

Brought the well in today. It was frantic and exciting at the drill site. I called for my new lawyer, Mr. Hamilton, to meet me at the rig, because I couldn't take the time to go into town; and I had to get the papers signed for more drilling permits.

One of the new workers made a comment about Ted's color that I didn't like. I knocked him down in one of the puddles of oil. He and Ted looked a lot alike.

My laughter gave away the fact that I had been listening to Jason and Alexia read the diary.

Jason asked, "James, have you heard about all of this stuff?"

I shook my head and responded, "No, sir. I've picked up bits and pieces over the years, but it sounds like you've got the whole treasure there."

Jason turned several more pages and read enthusiastically:

September 3rd, 1960.

Terribly hot in Ecuador. The laborers work so hard, I can't complain about the heat myself. They work like slaves but are happy all day long. I miss Hannah and the kids and keep telling myself I'm doing this for them, but I'm not sure it's worth it.

Hannah reminds me she married me, not a corporation, and the kids need a father, not another million dollars.

Jason considered this and voiced his thoughts. "I used to think he only thought about his work and never considered his family at all. But now I know he struggled with it just like everyone in the family did."

Alexia said, "You don't have to come from a multimillionaire international corporate family to deal with that. I used to feel guilty when I was working, because I wasn't spending time with Emily; but when I was home with her, I felt guilty, because I thought I ought to be working to earn the money we needed."

"I guess everyone deals with the same thing," Jason responded. "It's just that it looks different from your own perspective, and it's hard to see it through someone else's eyes."

Jason searched for a moment through the pages and then read:

November 18th, 1998.

Board meetings again all day today. Hamilton told me one of the new board members asked when I was going to retire so we could get a new CEO. I told Ted to tell him we may need a new board member, but we're keeping our CEO. Ted laughed and said he'd already told him.

I guess neither of us wants to be the first one to sit on the porch in a rocking chair. First, I did it for the money, then I did it for other people, but now I work because I love it. It's not only what I do, but it's who I am.

Alexia sounded thoughtful as she said, "It's almost like he's here with us, telling us what he's thinking."

Jason laughed harshly and said, "For me, it's actually better than when he was here in person, because I never stopped to listen or think at all. When he was here, it was like he didn't exist; and now that he's gone, he's more alive than ever in the pages of this diary."

Alexia took the diary and began to read. "Here's the last entry in the Work section. There's no date on it, and his handwriting is pretty shaky."

Talked to Gus Caldwell today and told him I needed him to do me a favor and teach Jason about the gift of work. Gus said he would take care of it, and he had a special job in mind for the young man. I hope Jason learns as much from Gus as I did.

It's great to be a financial success and run all these corporations, but it can't take the place of doing an honest day's work and being able to see what your own hands and your own labor have done at the end of the day.

As Jason and Alexia talked softly about their hopes, dreams, and plans for their future work, I focused extra attention on my driving. Maybe I would never be a multimillionaire head of a corporation or even be able to build a fence on Gus Caldwell's ranch, but I could sure be the best limousine driver in the world; and thanks to my boss and old friend, Red Stevens, I knew that being the best limo driver was a good thing to be.

Money can help us along our journey
and buy us a vehicle for the trip,
but it is never a destination.

FOUR

The Journey of Money

Traffic was light as I drove along the highway. It was a beautiful afternoon. Jason and Alexia were still basking in the glow of their wedding, and all of us were relishing the fact that, through the DVDs and the pages from his diary, Red Stevens seemed to be among us once again.

Alexia wanted to take a break and change out of her wedding dress. Jason agreed he'd had about as much of wearing a tuxedo as he wanted, so I spotted a suitable rest stop that looked like it would meet everyone's needs.

I helped Alexia and Jason out of the backseat and assisted them in getting the luggage they needed out of the trunk. As they walked up the hill to the building to change, Jason turned and called back to me.

"Feel free to look at the diary. We'll be back in a few minutes."

When I was a little boy, my grandmother had read me a story about a goose that laid golden eggs. I hadn't thought of that story in many years, but when I picked up Mr. Stevens' leather-bound diary, I thought it must be as fragile as an egg and as valuable as gold.

I carried it with care to a nearby picnic table where I could sit in the sun and read. As I opened the cracked and worn leather cover, I could almost feel the decades of blood, sweat, tears, hopes, and dreams that had gone into this diary.

I read the title of the second section:

The Gift of Money

I remembered a long-ago conversation I had with Mr. Stevens shortly after I began working for him. He had asked what I did with the money I earned. I told him that I tried to save some out of each of my checks and give some away every time I got paid.

He asked if I had any financial goals for my future, and I told him I was very happy and had everything I wanted. I remember he laughed and said, "James, that makes you a wealthier man than me, because I still have many goals yet to reach."

I sat there at the picnic table many years later and wondered if he had wanted too much or if I had somehow not been ambitious enough.

The first entry read:

January 14th, 1934.

Money is scarce, food is scarce, and Mom and Dad seem to be afraid. I've been trying to find odd jobs to bring some money in, but grown men can't find work, so no one wants to hire a kid.

I was deep in thought, thinking about those tough times during the Depression, and I didn't realize Jason and Alexia had returned and joined me at the table. I must have appeared startled.

Alexia said, "Sorry, James. We didn't mean to scare you."

I replied, "No, ma'am. I was just thinking about how a financial downturn hurts everyone and how people during the Depression struggled to get by with almost nothing."

I handed Jason the diary and hurried to get the luggage stowed in the trunk and hold open the door as Jason and Alexia resumed their places in the backseat.

As I was thinking about the desperate words billionaire Red Stevens had written during a time when he had nothing, I heard him speak from the DVD he had made for Jason.

"Today, we are going to talk about what may, indeed, be the most misunderstood commodity in the world. That is, money. There is absolutely nothing that can replace money in the things that money does, but regarding the rest of the things in the world, money is absolutely useless.

"For example, all the money in the world won't buy you one more day of life. That's why you're watching this videotape right now. And it's important to realize that money will not make you happy. I hasten to add that poverty will not make you happy either. I have been rich, and I have been poor—and all other things being equal—rich is better.

"Jason, you have no idea or concept of the value of money. That is not your fault. That is my fault. But I am hoping in the next thirty days, you can begin to understand what money means in the lives of real people in the real world. More of the violence, anxiety, divorce, and mistrust in the world is caused by misunderstanding money than any other factor. These are concepts that are foreign to you because money to you has always seemed like the air you breathe. There's always more. All you have to do is take the next breath.

"I know that you have always flashed around a lot of money and spent it frivolously. I take responsibility for this situation because I deprived you of the privilege of understanding the fair exchange between work and money."

Alexia picked up on the theme and read from the diary:

September 2nd, 1937.

I worked a full shift today and half of another in the fields. Harvest time is good, and the days are long enough to get in the extra hours. I earned almost a dollar. After eating and paying for my part of the room I'm sharing, I have 34 cents to add to my bankroll. It's not much yet, but I'm on the positive side of the ledger. At least I'm adding and not subtracting.

Alexia put voice to her thoughts. "It's hard to imagine a man who had billions of dollars started out with literally pennies."

"Yeah," Jason replied. "I never knew him when he wasn't one of the richest men in the world. I was actually embarrassed and ashamed in some weird way because of the wealth we had. It seemed like so much a part of him that I never imagined him being poor."

I heard myself speak before I thought. "Mr. Stevens, if I might interject …"

I saw Jason look at me in the mirror and nod.

"Your grandfather told me that he had been broke many times in his life but never poor. Red Stevens believed that broke was a financial condition and poor was a mental or emotional condition. He told me that broke was temporary, but being poor was permanent unless you changed your thinking.

"I thought a lot about it and came to realize that he was right. Working for your grandfather, I met a lot of very wealthy people that I would consider poor."

Alexia chimed in. "Jason, when you first met me, I couldn't even pay my rent, and you actually covered my deficit from the money you had earned building that fence at Gus Caldwell's ranch."

Jason nodded and agreed. "I remember that, but I never thought of you as poor. You and Emily were struggling with her disease, and Mr. Hamilton had given me the money along with my grandfather's instructions to find a place it would do the most good."

Jason read aloud from the diary:

October 11th, 1957.

Ted Hamilton called today to tell me the bookkeepers say I became a millionaire in August. It's funny to think that I've been a millionaire for almost two months and didn't even know it. I thought I would feel different than I do.

I told Hannah tonight at dinner, and she just smiled and nodded like she did when I told her I put the mail on the hall table. I will have to think on this.

Alexia sounded bewildered. "Wow, he became a millionaire and didn't understand it any better than I do."

Jason read another entry:

March 22nd, 1961.

Today, they dedicated the Stevens wing at the hospital. It was the best $4 million I ever spent. It seems like some of the most fun I have with money is giving it away. It certainly makes the toys I buy for myself seem more fun and feel better. I wish I had discovered this earlier.

Jason cleared his throat and read on:

June 7th, 1971.

On the cover of Forbes magazine this week. It's the first time the press has branded me a billionaire. I will have to call the accounting office to check.

Everything seems the same. There are just more zeroes. If money were all that someone had, they would be really poor.

I spoke up. "That's what he was telling me about when he described the difference between poor and broke."

Alexia turned several pages and read:

December 11th, 1984.

Ted got the money shifted to the foundation to buy the Christmas presents for all the boys' homes. I warned him that he'd better not hand out any of the packages until I get there.

I reminded him that Santa Claus was a white guy. He disagreed and reminded me I had never been to the neighborhood where he grew up.

It is as hard to give the money away responsibly as it was to earn it, but it's probably more fun.

I remembered the many trips when I had driven Mr. Stevens to the boys' homes he sponsored all across the country. Those were good times, and the boys had a way of finding the young kid still alive inside of Red Stevens.

Jason announced, "Here's the final diary page he put in about money."

It's getting late. Ted tells me that my financial house is in order, but I hope I have done the right thing. This will put a lot of pressure on Jason, and the rest of the family won't make it easy. I had the advantage of earning the money slowly over many years and learning the lessons that came along with the money gradually. Jason will have to get a financial education in a hurry. I think he's up to it.

Jason's voice shook. "I never knew he felt that way about the money and me and everything. I didn't understand he was trying to teach me the things I needed to know. You can't learn financial lessons using someone else's money. He made me earn money the hard way and then learn to manage it on my own. I wish I had known then what I know now."

Alexia said, "Well, at least you know it now, and if you forget, you've got the diary and the DVD and me and James. We won't let you down. Will we, James?"

I cleared my throat and stammered a bit but finally managed to say, "No, ma'am. I'm sure we'll all do what needs to be done."

I always remember Red Stevens repeating that if you want to learn how to manage money, you have to manage people; and if you want to learn how to manage people, you've got to learn how to manage yourself.

The limousine was silent for the next several miles as we all had our thoughts and Red Stevens' words for company.

A journey should never be judged by the
destination or mode of transportation.
It should be judged by the friends
who accompany us on the trip.

FIVE

The Journey of Friends

A s I piloted the limousine down the highway, holding it smooth and steady, my emotions were experiencing a roller-coaster ride. On one hand, there was the joy and promise of Jason and Alexia's wedding and new life together. On the other hand, being back at Emily's Home with the release of thousands of butterflies created bittersweet memories of a special little girl.

I was also struck by the fact that receiving the gift of insight from Red Stevens' diary left me with a feeling of joy and gratitude that I had known him as a boss, but at the same time, I felt the loss of my friend.

My thoughts were interrupted when I heard the unmistakable voice of Red Stevens on the DVD player giving another of his Ultimate Gift messages to Jason.

"*Friend* is a word that is thrown around far too easily by people who don't know the meaning of it. Today, people call everyone they know their friend. Young man, you're lucky if you live as long as I have and can count your real friends on the fingers of both hands.

"A friend is not someone who makes you happy all the time, but instead, they make you better. Friends share the greatest joys and the deepest sorrows you will face in your life, and you are privileged to share their highs and lows as well.

"Friends don't always tell you what you want to hear; they care enough about you to tell you what you need to know.

"Friendship is never a 50/50 even split. Both of you have to be 100 percent invested in the relationship, no matter what.

"The foundation of every friendship has to be trust and respect.

"Your friends will never be perfect, nor can they expect you to be perfect, but you both expect the other to always be striving to do better. Accepting the flaws of a great friend is like an investment you make in a valuable treasure. The investment seems insignificant compared to the reward.

"The whole world is looking for someone who will treat them like a friend. Instead of looking to find a friend, seek situations where you can be a friend, and you will always find what you are looking for."

As I was deep in thought, remembering all the many ways Red Stevens had been a friend to me, I heard Alexia begin to read from Mr. Stevens' diary:

August 4th, 1932.

Mother said I can spend all the money I had saved on a new base-ball glove for Billy's birthday present. She said this Depression won't last forever, and we always need good friends. My old glove's not that bad, and if it weren't for Billy, I wouldn't have anybody to play catch with anyway.

Jason and Alexia giggled in the back of the limousine as they thought of the powerful billionaire Howard "Red" Stevens as a boy whose most pressing decision had to do with a baseball glove.

I had to smile, myself, thinking about Mr. Stevens that way.

Alexia read another entry:

December 7th, 1941.

We just heard that the Japanese have attacked Pearl Harbor. None of us had ever heard of Pearl Harbor except for the fact that it is where the navy sent Billy. I talked to his parents, but we can't get any word.

Alexia continued as the emotion crept into her voice:

December 11th, 1941.

Everyone in town knew when the navy chaplain drove to Billy's house that it was bad news. They presented his folks with a folded flag and expressed the thanks of the president and everyone in America. It doesn't seem like nearly enough. I still can't believe he's gone.

Alexia began to cry softly, and Jason read the next entry about friends that Red had left for him:

January 4th, 1942.

I told my folks and Billy's that, after I graduate this spring, I'll be old enough to join the navy and finish what Billy started. It's the least I can do for my friend.

As I continued to concentrate on my driving, I replayed many past events in my mind. A lot of things fell into place that I had never known about before.

I had accompanied Mr. Stevens on many business trips to Hawaii. He never failed to spend several hours at the memorial on the USS *Arizona*. That's an emotional place for anyone, but it always seemed to have extra emotion and meaning for Mr. Stevens.

I remembered another time when Mr. Stevens was overjoyed as he let everyone know that Mrs. Stevens was expecting a child. I casually asked if they had any names picked out, and Mr. Stevens fell silent for a few moments, got a faraway look in his eye, and said, "We will name him Bill, and his friends will call him Billy."

Jason reverently turned the page and read the next two entries:

May 4th, 1972.

Ted has seemed distracted and under the weather for months. He's always dismissed it and said it was nothing, but I know there is something bothering him. When I have a problem, it's just easy to focus on the issue at hand, but when Hamilton has a problem, I worry about both the problem and my friend.

May 8th, 1972.

I played detective today and got Miss Hastings to tell me that Ted had been seeing a doctor at the medical center. I called the doctor to find out what was wrong with my friend. The doctor said he couldn't talk about it.

Money and power have their advantages. After I reminded the doctor that he worked in the Howard "Red" Stevens wing of the hospital, he opened up.

They are running some tests but fear that Hamilton has a serious kidney disease.

Jason sounded anxious as he read on:

May 14th, 1972.

Bad news today. Ted Hamilton has a terminal kidney condition. The doctor gives him less than a year unless he can get a kidney transplant. It is experimental and risky.

Jason continued:

May 16th, 1972.

The doctor tested my kidney, and I am a match. This is great news. The doctor warned me about the danger, but I told him I could live without my kidney but couldn't live without my friend.

I thought about all the years that Red Stevens and Mr. Hamilton worked together and were best friends. I realized that Mr. Stevens' sacrifice had given Mr. Hamilton half his life back; but on the other hand, I thought how Mr. Stevens' sacrifice had also given him his friend back.

We rode in silence for several miles and then Jason's cell phone rang. He was about to turn it off but checked the caller ID and said, "It's David. I'm going to take this."

Jason clicked the phone on and said, "Hi, David. Thanks for coming today. It meant a lot to have you there, and I know it's not easy."

He laughed heartily as he listened to his friend David speak.

Jason responded, "Well, it's good to have a friend like you, too, and I'll tell her exactly what you said."

Jason punched the button to disconnect and continued laughing loudly.

Alexia asked curiously, "So, what is so funny?"

Jason laughed even harder, unable to speak.

David was a young man Jason met as a part of his grandfather's Ultimate Gift experience. During one of the monthly challenges, Jason and David had become best of friends. David is blind, but it's easy to forget his impairment, because he is endowed with the most incredible sense of humor I have ever encountered.

He has taken what, for most people, would be a profound disability and turned it into an ongoing joke. He makes everyone he comes in contact with laugh and feel better about themselves. Outside of Red Stevens and Alexia, David has been the most positive influence on Jason's life.

Jason has gone from being a spoiled, entitled, rich kid to becoming a generous, formidable young man who is well on his way to making his mark in the world and making that world better for a lot of people.

Finally, Jason was able to control his laughter, and Alexia repeated her inquiry.

"So, what did David say?"

Jason announced, "David said to tell you that your wedding dress was the most beautiful gown he has ever seen."

Alexia was perplexed momentarily, then she joined Jason in another round of laughter.

It is amazing that someone can take his own pain and share it in a way that brings his best friend joy and laughter.

Alexia turned several pages in the diary and read silently for a moment. Then she spoke up so I could hear clearly. "James, you will want to hear this, I think."

I glanced at her in the rearview mirror and nodded.

She began:

June 22nd, 1988.

Another frustrating day on the mayor's zoning board. I'm going to remember to never volunteer for another political position like this. Very upsetting that they want to put the new freeway extension through James's neighborhood, and they are planning to tear down his house. I know he just did the renovations and added the new bedroom for the child they are adopting. A lot of hopes and dreams have gone into that house. Can't let this happen.

I was bewildered as I had no idea what this meant. It made no sense to me.

Alexia continued:

June 26th, 1988.

Everything is resolved. I had my engineers working on it day and night. After I donated a tract of land to the city and convinced everyone to move the freeway extension a mile south, everything will be fine. It's better for the city, anyway, and James won't ever have to move his growing family.

I was dumbstruck. I had driven Mr. Stevens to those very meetings he was writing about in his diary, but he had never mentioned a word about this to me. When I inquired how his meetings went, he always just shrugged dismissively and said, "Nothing special. Everything's going the way it should."

I remembered when the freeway extension had gone in. It had made our neighborhood much more accessible to the city and had increased our property value, but I never knew what my friend had done.

I glanced in the rearview mirror and saw Jason and Alexia both staring at me. I just smiled, shrugged, and said, "I guess it's good to have friends."

Jason spoke up. "Here is his final entry in the Friends section."

Tough day today. Feeling sick and weak. The only bright spot was when Ted stopped by. He said he had told the doctors he wanted them to take out the kidney and give it back to me, because it never worked right anyway, and he was hoping for a black model. We laughed and shared a lot of old memories.

It's good to know he will be there to take care of Jason and everything in the future when I'm gone.

Jason cleared his throat and spoke emotionally. "I guess true friendship isn't just for a lifetime, but it goes on forever."

I thought about the wonderful home that my family still enjoys to this day, a mile away from the freeway extension, and I thought about an old man laying a wreath on the memorial in Pearl Harbor.

Learning is a journey that never ends.

Each discovery reveals another
mystery waiting to be understood.

SIX

The Journey of Learning

I checked the mileage remaining in our trip and confirmed our route on my road map. The limousine is equipped with a state-of-the-art Global Positioning Device, but I have never trusted it entirely, and map reading is a skill my father taught me years ago. I'm afraid he would be distraught if he were alive today to see a whole generation of young people that can't find their way to the bathroom without some kind of computerized device.

My quick calculations told me that we would arrive at the beach house while it was still daylight. I thought it would be good to get the newlyweds settled and comfortable with their surroundings before dark.

Red Stevens' diary seemed like a magnet that kept drawing our attention to it. With the innermost thoughts and feelings of Red Stevens on every page in that leather-bound volume, it was hard to think of anything else.

Jason turned a page and read the heading on the next section of the diary that Mr. Stevens had prepared for him.

Jason read:

The Gift of Learning

I was eager to hear what Mr. Stevens had prepared to reveal to his grandson about learning.

Through my association for many years with Red Stevens, I met many successful and powerful men and women. It seemed to me that one of the things they all had in common is an intense curiosity to learn.

I remembered the first day I came to work for Red Stevens. He gave me three books and said, "This probably isn't everything you'll need to know, but it will get you started."

Two of the books were about being a chauffeur and driving a limousine. The third book he gave me was the operator's manual for the limousine.

The next week, when I was driving Mr. Stevens on a lengthy trip from town out to his ranch, he began talking about various chapters in the chauffeur's book as well as several things that surprised him about the wiring diagrams for the limousine that were pictured in the operator's manual.

I was shocked that he had read the books he had given me and relieved that I had read them as well. He talked about the books as if he had expected me to read them. This was because he *had* expected me to read them.

Jason inserted the DVD that his grandfather had made for him into the player. Mr. Stevens appeared on the screen on my dashboard, and I knew he was displayed on the larger flat screens in the back of the vehicle as well. He spoke about learning with great enthusiasm.

"As you know, I never had the benefit of a formal education, and I realize that you have some kind of degree from that high-toned college we sent you to that is little more than a playground for the idle rich.

"Now, before you get your feelings all hurt, I want you to realize that I respect universities as well as any type of formal education. It just wasn't a part of my life. What was a part of my life was a constant curiosity and desire to learn everything I could about the people and world around me. I wasn't able to go to school very long after I learned to read, but the ability to read, think, and observe made me a relatively well-educated man.

"But learning is a process. You can't simply sit in a classroom and someday walk offstage with a sheepskin and call yourself educated. I believe the reason a graduation ceremony is called a commencement is because the process of learning begins—or commences—at that point. The schooling that went before simply provided the tools and the framework for the real lessons to come.

"In the final analysis, Jason, life—when lived on your own terms—is the ultimate teacher. My wealth and success have robbed you of that, and this is my best effort to repair the damage."

I thought back and remembered that shortly after Mr. Stevens' funeral, Mr. Hamilton presented The Ultimate Gift and the twelve life lessons to Jason. The Gift of Learning involved Jason traveling to a remote village in South America to work in a library that had been funded by his father and grandfather.

Jason learned many things about his family and the world. He survived being kidnapped by dangerous members of a drug cartel but escaped with a very special friend of his grandfather.

Jason read one of the handwritten entries from the diary:

June 4th, 1931.

School is out today for summer vacation. Granddad is going to come by and take me to get a surprise. I hope it's ice cream.

Jason continued:

June 5th, 1931.

Granddad took me to the library and got me a library card of my own. I wanted ice cream, but I read some of the books last night, and I think this will be a good summer.

Jason exclaimed, "Wow, look at this!"

"It's hard to believe," Alexia chimed in.

I glanced back in the mirror to be certain everything was all right. They both looked up at me, and Jason held up a worn and yellowed card and simply explained, "His library card."

Alexia took the diary, carefully turned a worn page, and read:

August 14th, 1942.

Another day at sea. We are patrolling for enemy submarines, which creates a lot of boredom punctuated with brief moments of terror. I think I would go insane except that one of the older guys showed me that we have a pretty extensive library onboard. I can lose myself here for hours, and it feels like being back home in our little town library, except back there I've read all the books, and these new books here should keep me busy for a while.

Alexia turned another page, read silently for a moment, then chuckled and said, "Listen to this."

September 12th, 1948.

I'm checking out every book in the library and reading everything I can find about new techniques in the oil business. It's funny. Whenever I get a book from the librarian, they stamp it and write my name on the slip inside. I always look to see who has read the book before me. I've yet to read a book that Gus Caldwell hasn't already checked out.

We all laughed, but Alexia continued. "No, wait. There's more."

September 21st, 1948.

I stopped in to the library on my way back out to the oil fields. The librarian was just putting some brand-new books in the catalog. I found a great title about new ways to study geology for oil and gas producers. When the librarian wrote my name on the sheet, I was pleased to see that I was the first one to check it out, but when I turned the page, it had been stamped: "This book donated by Gus Caldwell." Under it, he had written, "Red, read chapter 4."

We all laughed heartily, and it felt almost like Red and Gus were there with us.

Alexia turned another page and exclaimed, "Oh, what's this?"

She handed Jason an envelope that had been tucked between the pages.

Jason spoke solemnly. "It's in a United States Navy envelope."

Jason opened the envelope and slowly unfolded an old and yellowed page. He read, "Dear Red, if you're reading this, I am gone. Don't worry for me as I am where I wanted to be, doing what I wanted to do. Please check on my folks and do me one favor. My mother loves poetry, but she never learned how to read, herself, and it always embarrassed her. From time to time, it would mean a lot to me to know that you would go and check on her and read a couple of poems. You always had a feel for that sort of thing. More than me. I liked some of the poems you wrote better than the ones in the books.

"Thank you for doing this for me and for being the best friend anyone ever had. Billy."

Alexia wiped away a tear and spoke. "Jason, I never knew your grandfather wrote poetry, did you?"

Jason seemed bewildered and replied, "No, that's news to me."

I smiled contentedly, remembering some of the long road trips when Mr. Stevens would read poems aloud from a book or even occasionally share one of his own.

Jason selected another page of the diary and read aloud:

March 9th, 1982.

Buried Billy's mom today. I was glad I was there, because not many people came. The minister said I could say a few words, so I read one of her favorite poems and placed it in the casket before they closed the lid. I hope, somehow, she can share the poem with Billy today.

Jason sounded startled. "He wrote the poem here on the page. Do you think I should read it?"

I spoke up. "Sir, if I may. Not only do I think you should read it, but, knowing your grandfather, I can say he would expect you to read it and read it well."

Jason cleared his throat and began. "It's entitled 'Cornerstones.'"

If I am to dream, let me dream magnificently.
Let me dream grand and lofty thoughts and ideals
That are worthy of me and my best efforts.

If I am to strive, let me strive mightily.
Let me spend myself and my very being
In a quest for that magnificent dream.

And, if I am to stumble, let me stumble but persevere.
Let me learn, grow, and expand myself to join the battle renewed—
Another day and another day and another day.

If I am to win, as I must, let me do so with honor, humility, and gratitude
For those people and things that have made winning possible
And so very sweet.

For each of us has been given life as an empty plot of ground
With four cornerstones.
These four cornerstones are
The ability to dream,
The ability to strive,

The ability to stumble but persevere,
And the ability to win.

The common man sees his plot of ground as little more
Than a place to sit and ponder the things that will never be.
But the uncommon man sees his plot of ground as a castle,
A cathedral,
A place of learning and healing.
For the uncommon man understands that in these four cornerstones
The Almighty has given us anything—and everything.

Alexia spoke energetically. "That is incredible. Does it say who wrote that?"

Jason was overwhelmed with emotion as he said, "It says, 'Written by *Howard Red Stevens.*'"

I remembered as if it had been the day before and not twenty years in the past when I first had heard that poem read aloud to me by the poet himself.

Jason turned to the final page his grandfather had compiled for him about learning and read:

I have learned so many things over the years but sit here now, at the end of my life, wanting to know more new things than ever before. I hope that when Jason's done learning everything from me and about me, he will find his own hunger to know what is unknown and see beyond the curtain.

As a hush fell over the limousine, I was certain that Red Stevens' wish for his grandson had been fulfilled.

Every life's journey is filled with problems.

These problems have solutions that create greater opportunities and more problems.

SEVEN

The Journey of Problems

J ason and Alexia talked excitedly and reread Red Stevens' poem. They were both stunned to learn of this new aspect in the multi-faceted personality of Red Stevens that they had never known. Jason turned to the next section of his grandfather's diary pages that Red Stevens had lovingly and thoughtfully selected for him.

Jason sighed deeply and said, "The next section is about problems. I never totally understood this one. Usually, I feel like problems are problems, and there's nothing good about them. Maybe later you learn something, but the problem itself is not good."

Alexia replied thoughtfully, "The things in my life that have brought me the greatest problems have also brought me the greatest joy."

I immediately thought of Emily and everything she had brought into the lives of everyone who had known her. Although she only lived a decade, she impacted more people in deeper ways than anyone I could think of. She was an amazing little girl who was full of life despite the fact she never really knew her father, and she and her mother faced many financial hardships.

Then Emily was diagnosed with leukemia shortly before Jason came into her and her mother's lives. Emily became part matchmaker, part strategist, and part tactician as she orchestrated people and events to bring Jason and Alexia together. I knew she would have been pleased but not surprised had she been at their wedding ceremony. Somehow, amidst all the butterflies and memories of her, I felt like she was there.

Jason reached for a DVD case and said, "Well, let's hear what he's got to say. Maybe it will make more sense this time."

A few moments later, Mr. Stevens began to speak.

"Jason, life is full of many contradictions. In fact, the longer you live, the more the reality of life will seem like one great paradox. But if you live long enough and search hard enough, you will find a miraculous order to the confusion.

"All the lessons I am trying to teach you as a part of The Ultimate Gift I am leaving you through my will are generally learned as people go through their lives facing struggles and problems. Any challenge that does not defeat us ultimately strengthens us.

"One of the great errors in my life was sheltering so many people—including you—from life's problems. Out of a misguided sense of concern for your well-being, I actually took away your ability to handle life's problems by removing them from your environment.

"Unfortunately, human beings cannot live in a vacuum forever. A bird must struggle in order to emerge from the eggshell. A well-meaning person might crack open the egg, releasing the baby bird. This person might walk away feeling as though he has done the bird a wonderful service when, in fact, he has left the bird in a weakened condition and unable to deal with its environment. Instead of helping the bird, the person has, in fact, destroyed it. It is only a matter of time until something in the bird's environment attacks it, and the bird has no ability to deal with what otherwise would be a manageable problem.

"If we are not allowed to deal with small problems, we will be destroyed by slightly larger ones. When we come to understand this fact, we live our lives not avoiding problems, but welcoming them as challenges that will strengthen us so that we can be victorious in the future."

As Jason turned off the video, he said, "All of that sounds good and may even feel good after you have found the solution to the problem; but at the time you're suffering through it, a problem is just a problem."

Alexia took the diary from Jason, opened it to the beginning of the section on problems, and read one of the entries:

November 17th, 1933.

Nothing but soup for dinner again tonight. We sat around the radio and listened to another of Mr. Roosevelt's fireside chats. He said that our nation needs to come together and support one another during this Depression. It's not easy when we can't even support ourselves.

Jason chuckled and said, "See? I don't see any benefit to that problem, and not much was learned from it other than depressions are bad—especially when you don't have enough food to feed your family."

Alexia turned the page and continued reading:

November 18th, 1933.

Mother told us this evening that we wouldn't have a Thanksgiving dinner since all we had was some vegetables from our garden. Doesn't seem like there's much to be thankful for.

Jason interjected, "Not much there. I don't know why he put it in the book for us to read. It doesn't seem like there's much that's special about these entries in the diary."

Alexia scolded him playfully. "Well, maybe if you would just show a little patience, it would make sense to you."

The couple laughed. Alexia turned the page and read:

November 19th, 1933.

I told Billy that we weren't going to have Thanksgiving this year, and he said their family really wasn't going to have a Thanksgiving dinner either because they had a turkey but no vegetables left and couldn't even come up with the ingredients for bread or pie. We told a couple of other friends, and everything came together.

Jason interrupted with a question. "What came together?"

"Patience," Alexia reminded him and continued:

November 30th, 1933.

A great Thanksgiving dinner today. The best ever. Everyone in the community came and brought what they had. We met many new neighbors and had a lot of fun. It all happened because I told Billy we weren't going to have a Thanksgiving dinner.

Alexia laughed aloud and continued, "See? I told you so. The problem had a solution that turned out better than it would have been before."

Jason laughed and agreed. "Yeah, it sounds pretty good. It's certainly better than our first Thanksgiving dinner together."

"You're not kidding," Alexia said. "I went to that mansion your family had and met all your relatives. They had all the turkey, vegetables, and other dishes that anyone could ever imagine, but it wasn't much of a Thanksgiving celebration."

Jason remembered and said, "They just wanted to get the inheritance my grandfather had given me as a part of The Ultimate Gift. They had everything in the world but couldn't find what those people had during the Depression."

Alexia responded, "That Thanksgiving dinner was the worst beginning I could imagine, but even with all the problems between there and here, all's well that ends well."

She held her hand in front of his face to let the sight of her wedding ring speak for itself.

She handed Jason the diary. He scanned another page and began to read:

November 22nd, 1963.

Today I have meetings in Dallas and then will be going to a luncheon to meet the president and hear him speak. We don't agree on everything, but he's brought a new excitement and energy to the country. I hope to learn more about him when we talk.

Jason turned the page with dread and continued to read:

November 23rd, 1963.

President Kennedy assassinated yesterday while we waited at the luncheon for him to arrive for his speech. The country is in turmoil and seems to have lost its direction.

Jason fell silent for a few moments, reflecting on that time and those events.

He turned the page and continued reading the words his grandfather had written long before Jason was born:

July 20th, 1969.

A great day. Neil Armstrong stepped on the moon, and we all watched it on TV. I couldn't help but think about JFK and the challenge he gave our country to put a man on the moon by the end of this decade. Although he's not here, President Kennedy's drive and spirit seemed to make this possible. His tragic death somehow brought us all together.

I sat behind the steering wheel just a few feet away from the newlyweds in the back of the limousine. I tried to give them their privacy while paying attention in case they spoke to me.

I had been too young to remember much about President Kennedy, and I was considering the possibility that something good could come out of a tragedy of that magnitude.

I heard Alexia begin to read another page from the diary:

March 20th, 1981.

Big scare today. Ronald Reagan was shot. I was praying and thinking about my friend and mentor as we stayed in touch with the hospital. When I heard his explanation of the attempted assassination was the simple phrase "I forgot to duck," I knew everything was all right.

Alexia turned to Jason and asked, "Did you know your grandfather was friends with the president of the United States?"

Jason responded, "I didn't have a clue. Obviously, there's a lot of things about him I didn't know."

Alexia directed a question toward me. "James, did you know Mr. Stevens was friends with President Reagan?"

I thought for a moment, considering how best to respond. "Yes, ma'am. I knew they were friends, and Mr. Stevens had a number of very significant friends. You would know some of their names, and others you would not.

"Mr. Stevens had the ability to deal with great people as if they were ordinary, and ordinary people as if they were great. It's one of the many things I admired about him."

Jason turned several pages and sounded confused and bewildered. "This doesn't look right."

Alexia leaned over and looked, inquiring, "What do you mean?"

Jason pointed and answered, "He didn't write this. Someone else wrote this last entry in the section."

Alexia held the diary close to her face and examined it. She nodded and said, "You're right, but just listen to this."

The doctor calls it another ministroke. I can't hold the pen or write any more, so this entry is being written by my night nurse, Lucy Spencer. Her handwriting's better than mine anyway.

Lucy has a similar but opposite problem with her daughter than I have been facing with Jason. Jason has the best of formal education but no experience or wisdom to take on the task I am leaving him. Lucy's daughter has had a lot of life experience and has developed a great deal of wisdom, but, due to financial problems, she wasn't able to finish her education.

I was very glad to be able to tell her about the newly formed Howard "Red" Stevens College Scholarship for the Daughters of Compassionate and Understanding Night Nurses. I think it's a good day all around.

Although I had visited Mr. Stevens every day he was in the hospital, and I had actually met the nurse mentioned in his diary, I had no idea of the interchange that had taken place in the middle of the night. Two people with diverse problems, trying to help one another, had somehow forged solutions and positive outcomes for each other.

I vowed that the next time I faced a problem, I would think of my old friend and employer as I looked for a positive solution and a greater good.

Our family is involved in our life's journey
long before we are born and long after we die.
Some of our family is connected by blood
and others only by love.

EIGHT

The Journey of Family

One of the books that my late, great friend and employer Red Stevens gave me on how to be a good chauffeur offered the advice to regularly check with passengers to see if they need to stop for food, water, or restrooms.

I asked the young newlyweds, Jason and Alexia, if they needed to stop for any reason.

Jason replied quickly, "No, I'm fine. Let's drive straight through."

Alexia coughed and cleared her throat in a very meaningful way. Not wanting to teach young Jason a lesson in the care and feeding of his new wife that I thought she was more than capable of teaching him herself, I replied offhandedly, "Well, I'm going to have to get some fuel here shortly, so we can stop, stretch our legs, and take care of any other needs that may arise."

Alexia replied cheerily, "Thank you, James. Apparently everyone in my new family isn't entirely clueless."

Jason was bewildered and asked, "What are you talking about?"

Alexia directed her question to me. "James, would you like to fill him in?"

Discretion being the better part of valor, I replied, "No, ma'am. I'll let you handle that. I'm simply proud to be included as part of your family."

Jason mumbled something and started the next video his grandfather had prepared for him. Once again, I heard the words of Red Stevens.

"Now, Jason, I realize that our family is about as messed up as a family can be, and I accept my full share of responsibility for that; however, the best or worst family situation can teach us a lesson. We either learn what we want or, unfortunately, we learn what we don't want in life from our families. Out of all the young men in the world, I have selected you. I have asked Mr. Hamilton to undertake this monumental task on my behalf for you. It's hard to understand why that means something, but I want you to know that it does.

"Families give us our roots, our heritage, and our past. They also give us the springboard to our future. Nothing in this world is stronger than the bond that can be formed by a family. That is a bond of pure love that will withstand any pressure as long as the love is kept in the forefront.

"It's important for you to realize that families come in all shapes and sizes. Some very blessed people are able to live their whole lives as part of the families they were born into. Other people, like you, Jason—through a set of circumstances—are left without family other than in name. Those people have to go out and create family."

Alexia opened Red Stevens' worn and tattered diary to the section filled with pages he had written over the years about his thoughts on family. She glanced down and began reading from the earliest entry:

February 16th, 1930.

Billy's parents came over tonight. Mother told us boys to go play outside so the grown-ups could talk. Later, they called us in to tell us, because of the financial depression, Billy's mother and father were going to have to go to another city and find work. They said Billy was going to be part of our family, and we would just all have to make the best of it. I know Billy will miss his family while they're gone, but I think this is great.

Alexia turned the page and spoke thoughtfully. "Can you imagine that times were so bad that people had to be separated from their children?"

"Yes," Jason responded, "but it sounds like my grandfather thought it was a pretty good thing."

Alexia read from another entry:

June 10th, 1930.

Billy's parents are back. They came to talk with my folks and take Billy home. Billy and I told them that, even though he was going back to their house, Billy and I would still be brothers.

Alexia continued looking through the pages and said, "Wow, this is interesting."

September 19th, 1939.

I met a girl today and told her she was going to be my wife. Her name is Hannah, and she told me if she ever felt the same way I might be her husband; but until then, I should mind my manners. I will try.

Alexia turned a page and read on:

December 28th, 1941.

Very hard Christmas with Billy gone. I told Hannah I was going to be leaving for the war sometime in the New Year. I told her I wanted to marry her but didn't think it was fair since I was going to go fight. She said she didn't think it was fair not to get married, and we are going to get married on New Year's Day.

Alexia squealed and said, "This is exciting. Listen to this."

January 1st, 1942.

Simple wedding. Just Hannah and our parents. I told her I wanted to do something better, but Hannah said the wedding is not important. The marriage is what counts. I vow to do better on that one.

Alexia read on:

August 16th, 1942.

Shipboard for many days. Guys who were strangers just a few months ago are now brothers. We have become a family. Every time we lose one, it's like losing a family member or a part of myself. The only thing that makes it worthwhile is remembering all our families back home.

Alexia said, "It's hard to imagine how young they were. They were a lot younger than us."

Jason responded, "Yeah, but I guess they just did what they had to do."

Jason looked at the diary and turned several pages, and then began to read:

June 6th, 1946.

Ruby is really bad. I stayed all night again last night at the hospital with Ted. It doesn't look good. I would trade places with her if I could, because I don't know if he can go on without her.

Alexia asked, "Who's Ruby?"

Jason sighed and responded, "Her name was Marietta Ruby. She was married to Mr. Hamilton when they were really young. They had known each other in school when they were kids and kind of grew up together. It was a tough time to be African-American in the South. She died shortly after they were married. Mr. Hamilton told me about her when I was in the middle of The Ultimate Gift year and getting ready to leave on one of my grandfather's challenges. The way Mr. Hamilton talked about her, I don't know if he ever got over her—even after more than fifty years had gone by."

Jason read the next entry:

June 7th, 1946.

Ruby passed away in the middle of the night. It seems impossible. I brought Ted home with me because I don't think he can take care of himself right now. Everything in his house reminds him of his Marietta Ruby. I'm hurting from his pain and my own.

Alexia asked, "Did Mr. Hamilton ever find anyone else?"

Jason shrugged and deferred the question to me. "James?"

I thought for a minute and then replied, "Mr. Hamilton has had many special people in his life as long as I have known him and long before that; but he never remarried, and there has never been another person for him like Marietta Ruby was."

I thought how difficult and poignant this conversation must be for two newlyweds on their wedding day as they were traveling to their honeymoon destination. Maybe Mr. Hamilton's loss then will remind them of all that they have here and now.

Jason read solemnly:

August 16th, 1994.

Hannah is gone. The cancer took her from me. I will never be the same. I feel empty.

There was a long silence in the car. I remembered that dark day. Mr. Stevens was never the same after that. Over time, he found a way to go on without her, but he focused much of his energy, time, and money on cancer treatment and research. I always thought he was still trying to do something for his beloved wife, Hannah.

Alexia glanced at several pages and then exclaimed, "Jason, here's a photocopy of a letter he kept, and it's from you."

Jason reached out and took the letter and looked at it.

He said, "Yes, I wrote this to him when he was in South America. It was in the Stevens library down there for years, and when I showed up, as part of his Gift of Learning for me, Bella, the librarian, had made a copy and gave me the original."

Alexia said, "Well, it must have meant a lot to him if he made a copy and kept it in his diary. Read it to me."

Jason began, "'Dear Grandpa: How is Ecuador? I miss you and Dad so much. You know my birthday is coming up. I was thinking, instead of giving me gifts this year, could you take me on one of your trips? I promise I won't cause any trouble. I just want to see you and Dad again soon. Write back, please. Love, Jason.'"

Alexia said, "It must mean a lot to you to know he kept a copy of it with him and how special it was to him."

Jason sighed and replied, "Yes, but there's so much I didn't know then and a lot I still don't know now. My grandfather was a complicated man with many good points and some that were not so good. He tried to fix the bad things late in his life. Somehow I feel like he's still reaching out to me and trying to make things right."

I didn't want to break the mood of the special moment the couple was having, but I had to have my say.

"Jason, I knew your grandfather for all your life. He didn't always know how to show it or say it, but he always loved you in a very special way. In the process of doing a lot of great things all over the world, he neglected some very important things at home with his family. When he realized this late in his life, he set a lot of things in motion to repair the damage he had done and to give you an opportunity to know the good parts of him and improve on the bad parts.

"Out of everyone in your family, he always knew that you and he were kindred spirits, and he was certain that you were the one who could carry on his legacy."

Alexia turned to Jason and reached out to touch him lovingly as she spoke. "Jason, Red Stevens was a great man, and he saw that greatness reflected in you."

Alexia turned a page and read, "Here's the last page he wrote about family."

My will, my estate, and The Ultimate Gift are all in place. I know I can count on Ted Hamilton, and I have the same confidence in Jason. I hope he will come to know that I respect him and love him.

Tears filled Jason's eyes as he spoke emotionally. "I wish I had known him in that way when he was alive. For most of my life, I was ashamed of him and wouldn't even claim him as my grandfather. I told everyone that Red Stevens was a rich uncle who just sent money but didn't really care. I wish I could tell him how much I love him."

I spoke up. "Jason, I believe I can speak for your grandfather, because, somehow, I'm confident he knows how much you respect him, and he feels your love."

Life's journey is often along a
rough and rocky uphill road.

Laughter can lighten the load.

NINE

The Journey of Laughter

Traffic was light, and we were making good time along the smooth highway.

Alexia spoke up. "James, I imagine you'll be running low on gas in the next ten or fifteen minutes."

"Yes, ma'am," I responded quickly.

Jason appeared confused as he looked from his new wife to me and back.

He asked Alexia, "How do you know whether or not we're running low on gas?"

Alexia laughed, shook her head, and said, "If you will allow me to quote my daughter referring to you, 'Guys are clueless.'"

It was only a few miles ahead when I spotted an exit to a small town that I was certain would be able to accommodate all our needs.

A limousine is a very comfortable way to travel. It has many comforts and conveniences; however, it is not a good way to travel if you want to be inconspicuous.

I found a gas station that was connected to a small diner in the middle of the picturesque little town. I topped off the gas tank with a few gallons of unneeded fuel as Alexia rushed to the ladies' room.

Jason and I noticed the limousine was drawing quite a crowd. The local residents seemed excited about the car but disappointed in us, as they were probably expecting a rock star or movie idol.

Jason called to me as he was walking away, "James, why don't you and Alexia meet me in the diner. We can get some coffee or a bite to eat."

I nodded and replied, "Very well, sir."

A few moments later, Alexia emerged from the restroom and spotted me waiting for her.

She stated, "James, we really needed some fuel. I'm glad you stopped."

I chuckled and replied, "Yes, ma'am."

She said, "Jason really is clueless. At what point in life do men begin to understand women?"

I realized I was on some pretty dangerous ground, so I simply replied, "I don't know, ma'am. I'm certain that would be at some point beyond my years."

Alexia and I made our way into the diner and sat down at a table with Jason. He had brought Mr. Stevens' diary in with him and was reading.

He said, "Listen to this. It's the first diary page he put in the section on laughter."

February 23rd, 1931.

Granddad came for dinner tonight. Vegetable soup again. I told Mother I would like a change. Granddad never said a word. He just took my bowl of vegetable soup and gave me his. I guess that was his idea of a change. We laughed a lot, and I think the soup tasted better.

Jason turned several more pages, scanning them briefly, and then read:

September 15th, 1942.

Rough seas for several days. It's been a long time since shore leave, and morale is low. The captain called for everyone to assemble after dinner. We were all nervous. He called everyone to attention and said we were all going to watch a film from the War Department featuring three experts in naval warfare. He said he wanted everyone to pay close attention and be prepared to discuss all aspects of the film when called upon.

The movie was the Three Stooges. We laughed until we cried. I think it's what everyone needed.

We drank some coffee, and Jason had a piece of pie before we walked back toward the limousine to resume our trip.

Alexia was thoughtful as she spoke. "Laughter is hard to understand sometimes. Things that were painful at the time can seem really funny later."

I nodded and agreed. "Yes, ma'am, you're right; and with that thought in mind, Gus Caldwell gave me a wedding present to pass along to you, ma'am, when I thought it was appropriate."

Jason blurted, "How come Gus sent a wedding present but it's just for her and not for me?"

I held the door of the limousine for Jason and Alexia as I responded. "Well, sir, I think you'll both get some use out of the gift, but the present is really for Miss Alexia."

I opened the trunk and took out the long package that Gus Caldwell had given me to present to Alexia. As I drove the limousine out of the little town and back onto the highway, Alexia opened the package.

She exclaimed, "Here's a note from Gus. It reads 'Alexia, congratulations on your marriage. If you have any trouble getting your husband awake and going in the morning, this may help.'"

Alexia reached into the box and pulled out a cattle prod. I couldn't help laughing out loud.

Alexia asked, "What is it, and what's it for?"

Jason explained. "It's a cattle prod. When I was working at Gus's ranch, I wasn't in the habit of getting up in the middle of the night and beginning work when Gus does. He thinks you're wasting time if you're not on the job when the sun comes up. Apparently, I didn't get up when he called me, so he thought it would be a good idea to apply this cattle prod to my backside."

Alexia joined in with me and laughed uproariously.

Finally, Alexia stated, "I think Gus Caldwell selected the perfect gift for someone getting married to Jason Stevens."

When the laughter subsided, Alexia stored the cattle prod in the back of the limousine so it would be handy for future use.

Jason slid a DVD into the player, and Red Stevens began speaking to us.

"This month, you are going to learn about The Gift of Laughter. The Gift of Laughter I want you to learn about is not a comedian in a nightclub or a funny movie. It is the ability to look at yourself, your problems, and life in general, and just laugh. Many people live unhappy lives because they take things too seriously. I hope you have learned in the last six months that there are things in life to be serious about and to treasure, but life without laughter is not worth living.

"This month, I want you to go out and find one example of a person who is experiencing difficulties or challenges in his or her life but who maintains the ability to laugh. If a person can laugh in the face of adversity, that individual will be happy throughout life."

Jason said, "I remember when Mr. Hamilton first played this message from my grandfather for me. I didn't understand it, but once I met David, I found a lifelong friend and a new understanding of laughter."

Alexia asked, "How did you meet him?"

Jason chuckled and explained. "Well, I was in the middle of the year my grandfather set up for me that he called The Ultimate Gift. I had already lost access to all the money in my trust fund, and he sent me out to meet someone who exemplified The Gift of Laughter. Since they had repossessed my car, I had to either walk or take public transportation."

Alexia laughed and interjected, "Yeah, I remember when I met you, you'd never been on a bus before."

"Right," Jason said, "but when I met David, I was actually riding the train, and he was sitting across the aisle from me.

"The seats on the commuter trains aren't always clean, so a lot of times when they're dirty, people will sit on a magazine. Since David's blind and doesn't know when it's clean or dirty, he always sits on a magazine."

Jason paused thoughtfully, seeming to picture the scene in his mind and then continued. "Well, this guy gets on the train and sees David sitting there with his dark glasses and cane and then notices the magazine. Apparently this guy wanted the magazine David was sitting on, so he walks over to David and asks if David was reading the magazine."

Jason began laughing as he went on. "David didn't even hesitate. He just stood up, turned a page in the magazine, sat back down, and told the guy that he was still reading the magazine but would be done in just a few minutes."

Alexia and I joined in the laughter. Then Jason became more serious as he continued. "I realized that if a guy could take a disability or a painful situation and laugh about it, it was good; but if he could take that same situation and make other people laugh about it, it was really great. David always seems to be able to make me and everyone else laugh, and that's a real gift."

Alexia turned several pages in Mr. Stevens' diary and then read aloud:

March 4th, 1952.

It's been a long, cold winter out at the well site. Ted invited me to go with him to an oil industry convention in Miami. I don't know whether I'll learn anything, but at least it'll be warm.

Jason turned the page and continued, "Here's an entry from a week later."

March 11th, 1952.

Ted and I are learning a lot in the meetings and took an afternoon off to go to the beach. Apparently, it's a white-only area. The security guy approached us and asked if everything was okay. I was mad and about to blow up, but Ted calmly told him we had come down to the beach to get a tan, and he was doing fine, but his friend, Mr. Stevens here, is still really pale and would like to make a complaint. We laughed the rest of the day. It's hard to be mad and laugh at the same time.

I thought about all the tough times Mr. Stevens and Mr. Hamilton had gone through dealing with racial issues in society. I hoped Jason and Alexia's children would know better times.

Jason read on. "Here's the last entry in the Laughter section. It looks like he wrote it from the hospital."

Sick today. I think the treatment may be worse than the disease. They brought me a clean specimen cup for another urine sample. I'm fresh out, so I filled it with tap water and left it for the guy. He came back and picked it up and said it didn't look right. I took it from him and told him he was right, so I drank it and said, "We'll just run it through again and see what happens."

It felt good to laugh. It brought a perspective to those dark days beyond hurt and sorrow.

Our dreams launch us on
every one of life's journeys,
and they are there to meet us at the end.

TEN

The Journey of Dreams

We were all still laughing from Mr. Stevens' lessons in laughter. I was struck by the fact that each of the humorous situations were not funny in and of themselves, nor were they even pleasant. I was thinking about people laughing through financial depressions, racism, disability, and even dying. I guess laughter is more of a perspective than a circumstance.

Jason slid the next of his grandfather's DVDs into the player, and we heard the lesson that had been prepared for him.

"Jason, this month you're going to learn about a gift that belongs to all great men and women—The Gift of Dreams. Dreams are the essence of life—not as it is, but as it can be. Dreams are born in the hearts and minds of very special people, but the fruit of those dreams becomes reality and is enjoyed by the whole world.

"You may not know it, but Theodore Hamilton is known far and wide as the best lawyer in the country. I know that performing at that level was a dream of his when I met him, and he has been living that dream for over fifty years. The dream came true in his heart and mind before it came true in reality.

"I can remember wandering through the swamps of Louisiana, dreaming about becoming the greatest oil and cattle baron in Texas. That dream became such a part of me that when I achieved my goals, it was like going home to a place I had never been before.

"I have been trying to decide, as I have been formulating this Ultimate Gift for you, which of the gifts is the greatest. If I had to pick one, I think I would pick The Gift of Dreams because dreams allow us to see life as it can be, not as it is. In that way, The Gift of Dreams allows us to go out and get any other gift we want out of this life.

"Jason, the best way to introduce you to dreams is to acquaint you with some dreamers. I knew many throughout my life. I always considered my friendship with the dreamers to be a treasure.

"One of the first truly great dreamers I ever met in my life had a passion to create places and things that would touch the imagination of people. This passion was with him all the days of his life. He had his share of setbacks and failures as well as many detractors. I never saw him or talked to him at a time when he didn't want to share his latest project with me. He was in the habit of creating huge dream boards that he would hang on the wall and draw out the plans for each of his projects on.

"I remember that when he was on his deathbed, he had arranged to tack the plans for his newest project onto the ceiling of his hospital room. That way, he could continue to look at his dream as he constructed it in his mind.

"A reporter came to visit him while he was in the hospital, and my friend was so weak he could barely talk. So, he actually moved over and asked the reporter to lie on his bed with him so the two of them could look at the plans on the ceiling while my friend shared his dream.

"The reporter was so moved that a person would have that much passion while dealing with a serious illness in the hospital. The reporter concluded his interview, said good-bye to my friend, and left the hospital.

"My friend died later that day.

"Please do not miss the point. A person who can live his entire life with a burning passion for his dream to the extent that he shares it on his deathbed—that is a fortunate person. My friend had his dream with him all the days of his life. It continued to grow and expand. When he would reach one milestone of his dream, another greater and grander one would appear.

"In a real way, my friend taught a lot of people how to dream and imagine a better world. His name was Walt Disney.

"But let me warn you. Your dreams for your life must be yours. They cannot belong to someone else, and they must continue to grow and expand.

"I had another friend whose name you would not know. He said it was his dream to work hard and retire at age fifty. He did, indeed, work hard and achieve a degree of success in his business. He held on to that dream of retiring, but he had no passion beyond that.

"On his fiftieth birthday, a number of us gathered to celebrate both his birthday and his retirement. This should have been one of the happiest days of his life—if his dream had been properly aligned. Unfortunately, his entire adult life had been spent in his profession. That is where he had gained a lot of his pride and self-esteem. When he found himself as a relatively young man without his profession to guide him, he faced the uncertainty of retirement. It was something he thought he had always wanted, but he discovered quickly it created no life-sustaining passion for him.

"A month later, my second friend committed suicide.

"The difference between one dreamer who was still energized by his lifelong passion while on his deathbed and another dreamer whose goal was so ill-fitting for his personality that he committed suicide should be apparent to you.

"Jason, it is important that your dream belong to you. It is not a one-size-fits-all proposition. Your dream should be a custom fit for your personality, one that grows and develops as you do. The only person who needs to be passionate about your dream is you."

"Wow," Alexia exclaimed. "Did you know that your grandfather knew Walt Disney?"

"No," Jason explained. "Not until I watched this video he made for me as a part of The Ultimate Gift."

Alexia said, "I went to Disney World several times when I was a young girl, but after hearing this story about Walt Disney, I think I would like to go there again."

Jason thought for a moment then nodded and said, "Me, too. It's a date."

Alexia thumbed through the diary, settled on a page, and began to read:

May 11th, 1933.

I walked to Bishop's Store to buy Mother a birthday present. I couldn't find anything for 36 cents, but it's all I've got. Mr. Bishop saw me looking at a vase and asked how much money I had. I told him, and he said it was on sale for 36 cents.

I know Mr. Bishop did that as a favor to me for Mother's birthday, but someday, I'm going to buy Mother a great birthday present and be able to help people like Mr. Bishop does.

Jason turned the page and read more:

May 14th, 1949.

I picked up Mother to take her to lunch today for her birthday. Then I took her to that big house on the corner with the rose garden she always admired. I told her happy birthday and gave her the keys. She loved the fireplace and pointed to the mantel and said she would put her favorite flower vase that I had given her for her birthday right there. It's a good day.

Alexia took the diary and read the next entry:

January 1st, 1952.

Cut the ribbon today on the Boys' Home. I've dreamed about this for years, but it's better than I thought it would be. The most fun I ever had with money is giving it away. One of the boys told me that having a home like this made his dreams come true. I told him, "Me, too."

I thought about how Mr. Stevens' dream for a boys' home had come true, but once the dream became a reality, it launched the dream to start many more boys' homes across the country. When Mr. Stevens passed away, there were dozens of them, and more will be built in the future.

Jason said, "You know, it's kind of like when I had the dream to do Emily's Home, but I only saw it as one facility in one city; but once we went through all the struggles and got it open, I realized that Emily's Home is something they need everywhere."

Alexia sounded emotional as she said, "I know it would make her happy. Somehow, you're making her dream come true."

Jason chuckled and said, "Well, Mrs. Stevens, I know one of her dreams came true today when you said, 'I do.'"

Jason took the diary back from Alexia and turned to the final entry in the section on dreams:

Sitting in the hospital like this has given me a lot of time to reflect on my life. I've come a long way since the Depression in Louisiana. Few people have ever been poorer or richer than me. It's all been good. I can't think about all the dreams that have come true without thinking about the dreams that are still floating out there, waiting to become reality.

Ted Hamilton and Gus will have to help Jason take it from here. Somehow I know he can make the rest of my dreams come true, and then his own dreams will be even bigger than mine.

Jason sat silently and reread the entire diary page that Red Stevens had written in his own weak and shaky hand while on his deathbed in the hospital. I felt the responsibility and the expectations that had been placed upon Jason. I was proud of him and glad to be along for the ride.

In life's journey, the things we keep we
eventually lose,
while the things we give
away, we always have.

ELEVEN

The Journey of Giving

A s I drove along the highway toward our beach-house destination, where Jason and Alexia would spend their honeymoon, I thought about Mr. Stevens' words and dreams.

All the dreams in my life seemed to be tied up in the big dreams of Red Stevens and now in the dreams of his grandson Jason. I guess some people have their own dreams, and others of us fulfill our dreams by helping special people along the way. Maybe it's like driving a limousine. You can't do a good job and help people reach their destination without getting there yourself.

Serving the Stevens family as my life's work means giving my time and effort toward making their dreams come true; but somehow, in the process, the dreams I have for myself and my family are a reality as well.

Giving and receiving are opposite ends of the same continuum. When you close the circle, they meet and come together.

I was thinking on these things as I heard Red Stevens' voice on another of The Ultimate Gift video lessons.

"This month, I want you to learn about The Gift of Giving. This is another one of those paradoxical principles like we talked about several months ago. Conventional wisdom would say that the less you give, the more you have. The converse is true. The more you give, the more you have. Abundance creates the ability to give; giving creates more abundance. I don't mean this simply in financial terms. This principle is true in every area of your life.

"It is important to be a giver and a receiver. Jason, financially, I have given you everything that you have in this world. But I violated the principle involved in The Gift of Giving. I gave you money and things out of a sense of obligation, not a true spirit of giving. You received those things with an attitude of entitlement and privilege instead of gratitude. Our attitudes have robbed us both of the joy involved in The Gift of Giving.

"It is important when you give something to someone that it be given with the right spirit, not out of a sense of obligation. I learned to give to people my whole life. I cannot imagine being deprived of the privilege of giving things and part of myself to other people.

"One of the key principles in giving, however, is that the gift must be yours to give—either something you earned or created or maybe, simply, part of yourself."

I heard Alexia begin to read from the Giving section in Red Stevens' diary:

November 11th, 1934.

Finally got my own job today. I deliver ice from 4:00 a.m. until school starts. It will be nice to make money of my own and help out the family, too.

Jason asked, "Why did he deliver ice?"

Being the eldest person in the car, I thought it fell to me to respond.

"Well, sir, I'm not old enough to remember it myself, but I understand from listening to my parents talk about it that, before refrigerators were available or before most people could afford them, they had iceboxes. A wagon would come around early each morning and deliver large blocks of ice that kept everything in the icebox cold."

Alexia turned a page and continued:

November 16th, 1934.

Delivering ice is really hard work. Carrying the 25 and 50 pound blocks up stairs is tiring. I'm really getting cold, too, in the early mornings. It's good to be working, anyway.

Alexia scanned another page and read on:

November 18th, 1934.

Granddad came over after school today and said he wanted me to have an old coat he had. It's a little big but fits pretty good. It will sure be nice to have it early in the morning while I'm delivering the ice.

Jason said, "Well, it's nice that his granddad helped him out."
"Wait," Alexia said. "There's more."

November 20th, 1934.

I learned from one of the men who works at the icehouse and knows Granddad that the coat Granddad gave me is the only one he had. I wanted to give it back to him, but I know he wouldn't take it, and he wants me to have it. His coat makes me feel warm inside and out.

Alexia scanned the diary and continued. "There's still more."

November 28th, 1934.

Got my first paycheck today. I went and bought a new coat for Granddad. He was excited to have the coat, and—I think—proud because I gave it to him. He told me it was good that one gift created another gift, and now we both have coats.

Jason spoke up. "You know, I have gone through most of my life thus far and never thought about the fact that there are people who don't have coats and what a great thing it is to give them one."

I wanted to encourage the seed in Jason's mind, so I said thoughtfully, "Jason, I think you're right. It's certainly something to think about. If there were a way to get people coats who didn't have them, it would be wonderful."

"Yes," Jason exclaimed. "It would be a way to honor my grandfather and his grandfather as well."

Alexia said, "It's amazing how giving one worn-out old coat can have such an impact and be a gift that could still be impactful today."

I was looking forward to the coming days and years when we might all learn the ways in which that one old coat might change the world.

Jason took the diary, turned a page, and read another entry:

January 14th, 1943.

We docked in Casablanca today. It's a beautiful city, but the poverty is overwhelming. I gave one little boy a candy bar as I was leaving the shipyards to explore the city. When I came back several hours later, he met me and gave me a picture he had drawn. I think the picture is a lot better than the candy bar.

"Look," Alexia exclaimed. "That must be the picture there."

Folded neatly and tucked into the pages of his diary that Red Stevens had collected for his grandson was, indeed, that picture from a little boy whom Red had met during World War II.

Jason described it. "Look. There's the ship, and that must be my grandfather in his sailor uniform."

Alexia picked up the narrative. "And there's the little boy standing next to him, holding the candy bar. They both have big smiles."

I kept my attention on the road as I drove, but in my mind's eye, I could see a young sailor far from home and a little boy in a poverty-stricken land connecting over something as simple as a candy bar and a child's drawing.

I think the value and worth of something can multiply immeasurably when it is given as a gift.

Jason read the next entry:

August 4th, 1948.

The oil well is producing really great output every day. It should be stable for a long time. I called the entire crew together that helped me bring my first well in and gave them the shares that Ted Hamilton drew up for me. This way, each of them will get a small piece of the fruits from their labor—hopefully for years to come.

Alexia responded, "That is something I would expect Red Stevens to do."

"Why do you say that?" Jason asked.

Alexia answered, "Don't forget. Emily was treated for months in the Howard 'Red' Stevens wing at the medical center."

"Yes, I remember that," Jason said, "but hundreds of people are treated there every year."

"No, this is different," Alexia explained. "Emily and I met your grandfather briefly while she was in the hospital. Like most everyone, your grandfather was quite taken with Emily, and I think she made a powerful impression on him. I didn't know it for a long time, but your grandfather paid all the medical bills."

Jason asked, "I didn't know that at the time. Why didn't you tell me?"

Alexia sighed and spoke. "It was around the time I met you, and everything was confusing. I didn't trust my emotions, and it was hard to accept that kind of gift, but he became very special to Emily and me. That's why she and I went to your grandfather's funeral."

Jason chuckled and said, "Yeah, I remember. I got there late and kind of interrupted the proceedings. It wasn't my finest hour."

Alexia patted Jason's arm and said, "We've all come a long way since then. Your grandfather has taught me—and is still teaching me—a lot about both giving and receiving. You can't have one without the other."

Here's the last entry he included about giving. Jason read:

I had a new night nurse last night. Her name is Pam. I asked her if the other girl was okay, and Pam told me she had traded so that she could take care of me. I asked why, and Pam told me that her grandfather had paid for her to go to college and nursing school with money he had gotten from oil well shares. She found out it was from my first well and wanted to thank me. I feel thankful to her and her grandfather. It's good to be a giver.

I thought about the little things people give to one another and how those ripples can extend out over many miles and many years. I remembered all the good times and generous acts that I had experienced and witnessed while working for Mr. Stevens. He had given millions of dollars and been honored many times, but some of his best gifts were tiny gestures that seemed to go unnoticed at the time; and then they returned in some beautiful way later.

Jason and Alexia spoke quietly between themselves, and I thought about the newlyweds and a special gift that I could give to them.

As we journey through life,
we must focus on the places we want to go
while we are grateful for all
the places we have been.

TWELVE

The Journey of Gratitude

My odometer, watch, and road map told me we were right on time and right on course. As an afterthought, I looked down, and the Global Positioning Device agreed. It's nice to know they can make new computerized technology that works as well as the methods we've been using for generations.

Sometimes I think the whole world is trying to grow up too fast, but I am grateful for the way things were, are, and will be. Working closely with Red Stevens for decades taught me that a person can be very thankful and joyous about what he has today while being hungry to be more, have more, and do more in the future. Like most things in life, it's a balancing act.

Jason played his grandfather's next DVD lesson.

"When you prepare your will and a video like this, you automatically have to think about your entire life. I have been so many places and experienced so many things, it is hard to remember that I have only lived one lifetime.

"I remember, as a young man, being so poor that I had to do day labor for food to eat, and had to sleep along the side of the road. I also remember being in the company of kings and presidents and knowing all the material things this life has to offer. As I look back, I am thankful for it all.

"During what, at the time, I considered to be some of my worst experiences, I gained my fondest memories.

"Jason, this month, you are going to learn a lesson that encompasses something that has been totally lacking in your life. That is gratitude.

"I have always found it ironic that the people in this world who have the most to be thankful for are often the least thankful, and somehow the people who have virtually nothing, many times live lives full of gratitude.

"While still in my youth, shortly after going out on my own to conquer the world, I met an elderly gentleman who today would be described as homeless. Back then, there were a lot of people who rode the rails, traveling throughout the country doing just a little bit of work here and there in order to get by. It was during the Depression, and some of these so-called hobos or tramps were well educated and had lives full of rich experiences

"Josh and I traveled together for almost a year. He seemed very old at that time, but since I was still in my teens, I may have had a faulty perspective. He is one of the only people I ever met of whom I could honestly say, 'He never had a bad day.' Or if he did, there was certainly no outward sign of it. Traveling about as we did, we often found ourselves wet, cold, and hungry. But Josh never had anything but the best to say to everyone we met.

"Finally, when I decided to settle down in Texas and seek my fortune there, Josh and I parted company. Settling down was simply not a priority in his life. When we parted, I asked him why he was always in such good spirits. He told me that one of the great lessons his mother had left him was the legacy of the Golden List.

"He explained to me that every morning before he got up, he would lie in bed—or wherever he had been sleeping—and visualize a golden tablet on which was written ten things in his life he was especially thankful for. He told me that his mother had done that all the days of her life, and that he had never missed a day since she shared the Golden List with him.

"Well, as I stand here today, I am proud to say I haven't missed a day since Josh shared the process with me over sixty years ago. Some days, I am thankful for the most trivial things, and other days I feel a deep sense of gratitude for my life and everything surrounding me.

"Jason, today, I am passing the legacy of the Golden List on to you. I know that it has survived well over one hundred years simply being passed from Josh's mother through Josh to me, and now to you. I don't know how Josh's mother discovered the process, so its origins may go back much further than I know.

"In any event, I am passing it on to you, and if you will be diligent in the beginning, before long it will simply become a natural part of your life, like breathing."

I was aware of Mr. Stevens' practice of daily listing things for which he was thankful. I was proud that he had shared that with me because he hadn't told many people about it. I hoped Jason and Alexia would adopt the practice. I can't imagine a better way to start a life together.

"Here it is," Alexia exclaimed.

October 22nd, 1938.

Josh and I have been together for quite a while, but now I know it's time for me to settle down in Texas and put down some roots. I've got a lot of things to get done in my life, and it's time to get started. As we parted company, Josh told me about his mother's Golden List. It gives me a lot to think about. I will miss him and think of him often. I wish him well.

"And here's the next day." Alexia read:

October 23rd, 1938.

Cold, hungry, and I miss Josh. I thought about the Golden List and fig-ured I should give it a try. I am thankful:

1. I am young and healthy enough to find my place and seek my fortune.

2. I grew up with a loving family that will welcome me home if I ever need them.

3. I'm not afraid of hard work. It has taught me much.

4. I have many good friends who will stand with me when I need them.

5. I have a best friend like Billy who seems close to me, even though we're miles apart.

6. I know the value of reading and the power of learning, and there is a public library nearby.

7. I have a great sense of humor and have learned to laugh at myself and the world around me.

8. The weather is still warm and dry, and I know I will find a place to stay before it gets too cold.

9. Josh left me some food to eat, so I had a good breakfast.

10. I am thankful for Josh's mother and her Golden List. I think I will try it again tomorrow.

Jason spoke excitedly. "Wow, it's so amazing to hear him talk about the Golden List on the video and then see it in his own handwriting that he wrote over a half century ago."

Alexia seemed distracted, and finally Jason pretended to scold her. "Are you listening to me at all, or am I going to have to get out the cattle prod?"

Alexia chuckled and said, "I'm sorry. I was just thinking about what he said, and I was trying it."

"Trying what?" Jason asked.

Alexia smiled and replied, "The Golden List. It really works."

Jason asked, "Will you share your list with me?"

Alexia began haltingly. "I've never done this before, but if I'm ever going to be thankful, it should be today, so here goes:

"1. On our wedding day, I'm thankful for you and the fact that I found my soul mate.

"2. I'm thankful for the years I had with Emily and that she brought us together.

"3. I am thankful that you and Mr. Hamilton won the court case so you will be able to continue your grandfather's work.

"4. I am thankful that Miss Hastings and Mr. Hamilton will always be there to help us.

"5. I am thankful Gus Caldwell is in our life and that he gave me a cattle prod to keep you in line."

Alexia laughed playfully but then solemnly continued her list.

"6. I am thankful that our wedding was beautiful, and we are going on a great honeymoon to the beach house.

"7. I am thankful that Red Stevens was a great man, and he recognized the potential in you.

"8. I am grateful that your grandfather gave you the twelve Ultimate Gift video lessons so we can have them for the rest of our lives.

"9. I am thankful that your grandfather selected diary pages he had written throughout his life, and he cared enough to put them together in this special book."

Alexia fell silent, and Jason blurted, "And what about number 10?"

"Just be patient." Alexia spoke a bit louder and directed her words toward me. "And number 10, I am thankful for James and the things he does for us. I am thankful he is driving us to our honeymoon beach house, and I'm thankful he will go everywhere with us from now on."

One of the chapters in the chauffeur's instruction book that Mr. Stevens gave me long ago says that a good chauffeur should remain unemotional and never reveal his feelings. I'm not sure the author of that book ever heard a young lady say what Alexia had just said about me.

I looked in the rearview mirror and quietly said, "Thank you, miss."

She met my eye in the mirror and just nodded.

Jason read another diary entry:

August 18th, 1994.

We buried Hannah today. I am grateful it was a clear day and not too hot. I am thankful that Ted and Gus were both with me. I am blessed that Hannah shared her life with me.

Alexia said, "It's amazing that, on the worst day imaginable, he found things to be thankful for."

Jason agreed and said, "Yes, maybe it's more important during the rough times than during the good times."

I remembered Hannah Stevens' funeral and the empty feeling that her death left with us all, but I had to admit I was thankful to have known her and that, through my work with the family, we had been a part of one another's lives. I thought that Jason was right in that the worst times are when we should be most thankful.

Alexia took the diary and turned several pages. She read:

I know now I will probably never leave this hospital. I am thankful for all the doctors and the nurses who take care of me. I have had so many friends stop by, and I have gotten so many flowers that they have started giving them to other people here in the hospital. It's a good day.

Jason and Alexia fell silent, and I was left with my thoughts of an old man on his deathbed who could proclaim his thanks for many things and declare it to be a good day.

As I thought of Mr. Stevens, I realized it was a good day—then and now.

Life's journey may last many years,
but to reach our destiny,
we must travel well each day.

THIRTEEN

The Journey of a Day

A s I drove along with my thoughts and memories for company, I thought about all the things this day had brought
forth.

Early that morning I had been scurrying about, preparing for a
wedding. Emily's Home is a wonderful facility for families dealing
with hospitalized children, but the building and the grounds were
not designed for a wedding.

Like many tasks, it seemed we would never be able to attend to
all the details before the appointed hour for the wedding ceremony,
but when that magic point in time finally arrived, miraculously
everything was in readiness.

It was wonderful to see old friends, new friends, and the Stevens
family gathered together for the occasion. Many members of the
Stevens family had experienced healing and forgiveness, but others
were still tending to old wounds.

Judge Neely did a masterful job conducting the ceremony. It
seemed fitting as his expertise in the recent legal confrontation had
gone a long way toward making Jason and Alexia's wedding day possible or at least harmonious.

After the couple exchanged vows, thousands of butterflies were
released in memory of Emily and the life she lived as well as the part
of her that still lives inside of all of us.

After the service, there was a brief reception that gave everyone
an opportunity to relax, greet one another, and congratulate the
newlyweds.

Just when I thought a single day couldn't hold any more joy
and emotion, Mr. Hamilton presented Jason and Alexia with a long-
planned wedding gift from Red Stevens.

What I thought would be a relaxing and quiet drive of several hours to the beach house where the couple would be honeymooning turned into a roller coaster of emotions brought out through the diary pages that Red Stevens had compiled for Jason and his new bride. Coupled with Red Stevens' video messages prepared for The Ultimate Gift bequest, those handwritten diary pages represented the essence of Howard "Red" Stevens' life from the perspective of one day at a time.

I heard the voice of Mr. Stevens from the DVD player.

"Jason, I want you to know that as I was contemplating The Ultimate Gift I wanted to present to you through my will, I spent a lot of time thinking about you. I think you gained a permanent place in my Golden List each morning. I am thankful that you and I share a family heritage, and I sense a spark in you that I have always felt in myself. We are somehow kindred spirits beyond just our family ties.

"As I have been going through the process of creating my will and thinking about my life and my death, I have considered all the elements in my life that have made it special. I have reviewed many memories, and I carry them with me like a treasure.

"When you face your own mortality, you contemplate how much of life you have lived versus how much you have left. It is like the sand slipping through an hourglass. I know that at some point I will live the last day of my life. I have been thinking about how I would want to live that day or what I would do if I had just one day left to live. I have come to realize that if I can get that picture in my mind of maximizing one day, I will have mastered the essence of living, because life is nothing more than a series of days. If we can learn how to live one day to its fullest, our lives will be rich and meaningful."

Jason turned to Alexia and spoke. "Today is our wedding day. I'm sure it is something you've thought about a lot. I hope it was everything you wanted it to be."

Alexia smiled, held Jason's hand, and said, "I think every young girl thinks about her wedding day for many years. I thought of it more like a fantasy or a fairy tale. Don't get me wrong. It was a great wedding with a wonderful group of our friends and family. It was special to have it at Emily's Home and to think about how she brought us together and how she remains with us in many special ways."

Alexia paused thoughtfully and then continued. "What I want you to understand is that I no longer think of a wedding as an end in itself. In fact, it's more like the beginning of everything. Your grandmother's words that Red repeated in his diary may have said it best in that the wedding isn't nearly as important as the marriage. But today will be special in my memories for many reasons. On top of the wedding, there is getting to share your grandfather's diary and The Ultimate Gift messages on the DVDs with you and James."

I thought about Alexia's words and how her perspective had changed over the years. I thought about her special feelings regarding today, and I was grateful that she had included me in a special way.

Jason read one of the entries from the diary:

June 17th, 1934.

A great day today. I hit a home run to win the game, and Billy and I teamed up for a double play. This is great.

Jason laughed and said, "I never thought of my grandfather as a jock."

"Let me read one," Alexia said as she took the book and turned several pages. She read:

November 29th, 1941.

Exciting letter in the mail today. Billy's ship is in Hawaii for a month, and he was able to get a letter off to me. He's doing well and sounds like a real sailor. I can't wait till I see him again.

Alexia stared at the page for a moment and then spoke solemnly. "In less than ten days, Billy was dead, the war started, and the whole world changed."

Jason said, "Yes, it's amazing how everything can change in just one day or even one moment."

I thought about the days in my life that had started out just like any other day, but then without notice, everything changed. I guess every day brings its own joys, sorrows, opportunities, and challenges. We've just got to take it one day at a time, and make the most of everything.

Alexia flipped a few pages back and read:

November 3rd, 1938.

Got word today that Granddad is sick. I am heading home as quickly as possible. He is on my mind and in my prayers.

Alexia turned the page and continued:

November 5th, 1938.

Got home too late. Granddad is gone. It's hard to believe. It seemed like he was so big and strong and would always be there.

Alexia read the next page:

November 6th, 1938.

Granddad's funeral today. It was sad but in some ways almost like a celebration. I never knew he had so many friends and people who cared about him.

Jason and Alexia fell silent, so I spoke. "We never know who will come into our lives or who will leave from day to day. One of the things I learned from Mr. Stevens was the ability to treat every day like a gift and every person like they are special. I started following Mr. Stevens' example because I thought it was the right thing to do. Before long, I realized every day *is* a gift and every person *is* special, so it just seems natural to value everything and treasure it all."

Jason held the diary, turned several pages, and read another entry:

May 16th, 1949.

Mother is thrilled with her new house. It's fun to be back in town and around her. I visited Granddad's grave today. I wish he had known who I have

become and what I have done. Maybe he knows. I miss him a lot and think of
him constantly. Many times when I meet a new person or face a new situa-
tion, I can almost feel him giving me advice and direction.

"I get it," Jason announced. "He had the same feelings about his grandfather that I feel about him. It's like living in the shadow of this giant, and you're never sure you can live up to what's expected of you."

Alexia said, "Jason, your grandfather loved you and respected you. He gave you The Ultimate Gift for a reason, and I know he believed—like I do—that your best effort will always be good enough."

I realized that Alexia had just given Jason the greatest gift anyone can ever receive. To know that the person who loves you best is the person who believes in you most and makes everything possible.

With Red Stevens' direction and Alexia's encouragement, I was excited to think about what the future might hold for young Jason Stevens.

"This is interesting," Jason said. "Listen to this:

October 17th, 1984.

Gus and I are hunting for a few days in New Mexico. Today was the
best day in many years. This little rancher who let us hunt on his place was
stretching some new fence. Gus and I forgot about hunting and built a fence
today. It's just like old times. I think we both miss those early days.

Jason laughed and said, "I remember those hard days down in Texas building that fence on Gus's place as part of The Ultimate Gift.

It never occurred to me that Gus and my grandfather really did that same kind of work and actually enjoyed it."

Alexia asked, "Wasn't it a good experience for you?"

"Yes," Jason answered, "but it wasn't good at the time. It was only good when I looked back on the work I did and the lessons I learned through the experience."

Jason spoke up so I could hear him clearly in the front of the limousine.

"James, if you or Alexia ever feel like I'm forgetting about The Gift of Work, I hope you'll just play my grandfather's DVD for me instead of making me build another fence."

We all laughed.

Alexia said, "Here's the final entry he wrote about The Gift of a Day. It's hard to read his handwriting."

Alexia tilted the diary to catch the light better and read:

A great day today. One of the best ever. I met some of my neighbors in the adjoining rooms here in the hospital, and we all had lunch together and watched the St. Louis Cardinals game on my TV. I have sat in the owner's box for many All Star games and the World Series, too, but I never enjoyed a baseball game more than today. I guess if you don't know whether or not you'll be around for the end of the season, today's game is really all that matters.

I remembered how much Mr. Stevens had enjoyed his baseball games and the St. Louis Cardinals. He was fond of telling everybody that if your name is Red, you've got to be a Cardinal fan. I never knew much about baseball or the Cardinals until I met Mr. Stevens, but I will admit that it's been a long time since I missed a game.

Alexia spoke up. "I guess we only think about a day as being special if something big happens, like our wedding today; but if you think about it, our lives are more about a lot of good things that happen on a lot of normal days that go unnoticed instead of the handful of days that we celebrate."

Jason said, "I guess since we never know what moments or days will turn out to be significant, we should treat each day as if it is special, and celebrate it all."

I knew I would remember that special day because of everything that had happened. I knew it would be a great day to look back on because—whether it would be a week, a decade, or a year in the future—thinking about Alexia and Jason's wedding day would remind me that, at every point in our lives, today is special.

Love is not a goal you reach
as part of your life's journey,
but something you give and receive
all along the way.

FOURTEEN

The Journey of Love

The afternoon was beginning to fade into evening. There is that certain point when colors begin to melt into shadow. Days like that one make you wish they would never end, or maybe they make you eager for tomorrow.

I knew we would be arriving at the beach house within ten or fifteen minutes. I had wanted to get Jason and Alexia there before dark so they could get comfortable with their surroundings, and I could get them settled in before I left them to enjoy their honeymoon. I calculated I would have just enough time to get everything done I needed to do with a little time left over for one special errand I had in mind.

Jason announced, "This is the last video he made for me as a part of The Ultimate Gift."

Jason slid the DVD into the player, and I heard Red Stevens.

"Jason, in this last month, I'm going to introduce you to the one part of my Ultimate Gift that encompasses all the other gifts as well as everything good you will ever do, have, or know in your life. That is The Gift of Love.

"Anything good, honorable, and desirable in life is based on love. Anything bad or evil is simply life without the love involved. Love is a misused and overused term in our society. It is applied to any number of frivolous things and pursuits; but the love I am talking about in The Gift of Love is the goodness that comes only from God. Not everyone believes or acknowledges that. And that's okay. I still know that real love comes from Him—whether or not we know it.

"Jason, we've come a long way in this Ultimate Gift. I want you to know, above all, that in spite of all the mistakes I made and the many times I failed you, that, Jason Stevens, your grandfather loved you."

A lump formed in my throat, and I heard Jason speak emotion-ally. "I have watched him deliver that message to me and heard him say those words many times, but I never fail to feel the love he talked about."

Alexia nodded and said, "I think that's one of the hardest things about love. It doesn't make sense. You can't touch it or see it. You have to simply feel it. It's hard to trust our feelings on something so important."

Alexia held Jason's hand and continued. "When I first met you, you were trying to live up to your grandfather's will so you could get your inheritance. I didn't trust your motives or my feelings. I was dealing with losing Emily and finding myself, but deep down, I knew that if it was right between us, it would work regardless of what I did or even in spite of what I did."

Jason replied, "I just know that I started out only wanting money from my grandfather, and somewhere along the line, I forgot all that and realized that no amount of money or things would mean anything if I didn't have you."

A good limo driver knows when to become silent and invisible. When a newlywed couple wants to discuss love on their wedding day, it's a good time for a guy like me to focus on his driving.

Eventually, I heard Jason reading an entry from his grandfather's diary:

January 30th, 1934.

An ambulance came today and took Mother to the hospital. She's been sick for a couple of days, but she always got well before. Granddad

said they've got her in a special treatment area, and we can't visit. I
hope she knows how much I love her. I think I forget to say it often
enough.

He turned the page and continued:

February 9th, 1934.

A great day today. Mother is home. Granddad said we had to let her rest,
but I snuck in and waited till she woke up and told her that I loved her. I told
her not to tell Granddad. She said she loved me, and everything would be
okay. I believe her.

It made me think about my parents, my wife, my kids, and all
the special people in my world. I never tell them that I love them
nearly enough. You can get tired of hearing almost anything except
the words "I love you" from a special person in your life.

I had many great days with my boss and friend Red Stevens, but
the very best would have to be that last night at the hospital as I was
leaving. I thought he was sleeping, and I had already turned out the
light to go when I heard his voice say, "James, take care of Jason, and
be sure that he knows that I love him."

I thought he had fallen asleep again when he said, "And, James,
I love you, too."

The wrong words from the wrong people mean less than nothing, but the right words from the right people mean more than
everything.

Alexia held the diary and read:

January 10th, 1944.

We are steaming toward home and should make it back to America tomorrow. I just love the sight and sound of that word: America. I have lived my life until now without thinking about it, but I don't think I'll ever forget how much I love my country. I didn't know how I felt about it until I discovered I was willing to fight and die for America and all that it means. It's what makes everything now and in the future possible.

Jason turned the page with anticipation and read on:

January 11th, 1944.

As the sun was coming up today, we entered New York Harbor and passed the Statue of Liberty. She was the most beautiful woman I had ever seen until I saw Hannah waiting for me at the pier. All my hopes and dreams seem to be in one place at one time. I do not have the words to express the love I feel.

I think the Greeks had it right. Mr. Stevens told me one time that, in Greek, there are seven words for love. In English, we might love our dog, the St. Louis Cardinals, our spouse and children, and our country, but we only have one word to cover it all. Mr. Stevens thought that our deeds have to take over where our words fail us.

When we can't tell people exactly how we feel about them, we have to show them.

Alexia read the next entry:

April 29th, 1951.

Our son arrived today. They wouldn't let me be there for the birth, but when I came into the room and Hannah was holding him, all the love I had felt in my life—all put together—was nothing compared to the love I felt for them at that moment. I am filled with joy and gratitude.

Alexia turned the page and continued:

May 2nd, 1951.

Hannah is doing great. The doctor said she should be able to go home tomorrow. Hannah knew how I felt about the name Billy. She held my hand and said, "Yes, let's call him Bill." Someday I will tell my son about Billy and how he lived and died. I hope I can make him understand.

Alexia scanned several pages and cried, "Wait till you hear this!"

She cleared her throat as if preparing to make an important announcement, then spoke:

May 19th, 1984.

My grandson was born today. Difficult delivery, but mother and baby are fine. They finally let me hold him. He looked at me as if he knew what

I was thinking. The nurse said that's not possible, but I know different. Young Jason Stevens and I are connected in some special way. Wait and see.

"That's amazing," Jason exclaimed. "He never told me. I had no idea …"

Alexia said thoughtfully, "Maybe he tried to tell you, and you weren't ready to listen, or maybe he didn't know what to say."

The couple fell silent, so I spoke up. "Whatever the case, I know that your grandfather loved you, and The Ultimate Gift lessons, along with that diary, are his way of saying what needed to be said."

Jason held the diary lovingly and looked at it as if seeing it for the first time. He turned several pages with care and spoke. "Here's the last page in the book."

It's getting very late. This will be my last entry in my diary. It's been a lifelong habit I have relished. I've got just enough time left to get some of the special pages organized for Jason. I hope the things that I couldn't tell him during my life I can somehow share with him after my death. I made many mistakes and left a lot of things undone. I hope he knows I did my best, and I love him.

Alexia cried softly, and Jason wiped away several tears. The love seemed like a tangible thing that could be touched or held in your hand. Love never dies. It lived on beyond Red Stevens' life. Somehow love from the past can be felt in the present and accompany us on our journey into the future.

As we journey into our future,
we begin to understand our past
in ways that help us travel today.

FIFTEEN

The Ultimate Journey

My road map, watch, and the limousine's odometer confirmed, once again, that the Global Positioning Device was actually working. I exited the highway and slowly turned onto a two-lane state road that would take us to the coast.

Jason pushed a button on the panel in the back of the limousine, and the giant sunroof slid open. As we wound our way along the state road, fresh air and the scent of the forest permeated the interior of the car.

A few moments later, I began to detect the tangy salt aroma of the ocean. A few miles further, I slowed the limousine as we entered a small coastal village. Jason and Alexia pressed their faces against the car's windows to get a good look at the quaint village that was the closest outpost of civilization to the beach house where they would be honeymooning for the next week.

As Jason and Alexia looked over the village, all the citizens seemed to stop in their tracks to stare at the limousine.

Alexia exclaimed, "There are several really cute shops here that should have everything we'll need."

Jason responded doubtfully, "What will we need?"

"Still clueless," Alexia replied.

Just as we were about to pass through the small village, I noticed one shop that I felt certain would meet my needs for the special errand I had been planning.

As quickly as the village had appeared, it vanished into the evening, and we were, once again, on a two-lane road, passing through an old and undisturbed forest.

Within a few minutes, I spotted the discreet sign that indicated the driveway to the beach house. The ocean smell was powerful. It conjured visions of distant lands and faraway places.

Shortly, the limousine rumbled across a one-lane wooden bridge over a small inlet. Then the beach house could be seen in the distance.

The crushed gravel driveway led directly to a porte cochere and circle driveway in front of the house. When you drive a superstretch limousine, you are always relieved to see a circle driveway for turning around, as backing up can be quite hazardous.

The house appeared to be everything the rental agent had promised. It was an old Cape Cod–style home that had been immaculately cared for. If one considered the inlet we had crossed, the beach house actually sat on a small isolated island.

I spotted a pickup truck parked near the house, so I knew that the caretaker was already there, just as promised, to show us around and get the newlyweds settled.

I pulled the limousine to a stop under the roof of the porte cochere and jumped out to open the back door.

Just as Jason and Alexia were emerging from the limousine, the front door of the beach house opened, and a tall middle-aged man stepped onto the front porch.

He smiled broadly and said, "Welcome. My name is Eddie Crisp, and you must be Mr. and Mrs. Stevens."

He walked down the front steps and shook hands with Jason and Alexia, saying, "And I believe congratulations are in order."

Alexia nodded and said, "Thank you, and this is our friend James."

I shook hands with Mr. Crisp, and he took charge, saying, "Come on in, and I'll show you around, and then we will get everything settled."

The front door opened into a large entryway. There was a stairway to the right, and an archway to the left that led into a great room with a stone fireplace and wonderful old furniture and artwork; but it was hard to notice anything other than the wall of windows that offered an unobstructed view of the ocean. Double doors opened onto a redwood deck with wide stairs that led directly onto the beach.

As Mr. Crisp showed Jason and Alexia the kitchen, library, and other features of the home, I stepped out onto the deck to take it all in.

Red Stevens had always been fond of referring to one of his favorite authors who said that our world is made up of three primary elements: the earth, the sea, and the sky. Only at the shore do all three come together.

I gazed at the incomprehensible expanse of the ocean that stretched out before me. In the far distance, I could see one solitary light that I knew must be a cruise ship or a freighter. I thought briefly about Mr. Stevens, his childhood friend Billy, and all those brave men and women who had served at sea during wartime when spotting a light on the horizon could signal either a friend or enemy.

I walked down the redwood stairs and stepped onto the hard-packed sand of the beach. As I had hoped and planned, there was more than enough light left in the day for Jason and Alexia to explore what would be their new home and surroundings for the week.

The breeze was fresh, and the soothing sound of the waves lapping onto the beach caused one to realize that all his great problems and endless worries probably didn't matter.

I was startled to hear steps on the deck behind me and turned to see Jason and Alexia walking toward the deck rail.

Jason called to me. "Everything's good in the house. Does it all look okay out here, James?"

I smiled and replied, "It couldn't be better."

I joined the couple on the deck, and Alexia said, "James, I'm going to need you to run me into town so I can pick up just a few things."

"I would be happy to, ma'am," I offered, "or if you would make a list for me, I will unload your luggage and then drive into town and pick up your items while you two are getting unpacked and settled."

A few minutes later, armed with Alexia's shopping list, I was piloting the limousine across the wooden bridge and back into town.

A drugstore proprietor helped me quickly find everything on Alexia's list, and as I was paying for the items, he asked, "Does that limousine belong to somebody rich, powerful, or famous?"

I smiled and nodded, replying, "Yes, sir, and a whole lot more."

At the end of the main street, near the edge of the small village, I parked in front of the gift shop I had seen earlier. As I got out of the limousine, a middle-aged woman emerged from the shop and locked the front door.

I called to her as I rushed toward the shop. "Ma'am, if I may, I have one vital purchase that I must make before you close."

She looked at me with consideration and then shrugged and unlocked the door. To be honest, I think the limousine impressed her more than I did.

As I told her what I wanted, she quickly led me to a shelf in the back of the store and pointed to an item. I picked it up and realized it was perfect.

I said, "I'll need two of these."

She replied, "People don't normally need more than one."

"Yes, ma'am," I responded, "but these aren't for normal people."

When I explained the situation, she helped me gift wrap my purchases and sent me on my way with a smile.

Back at the beach house, some wonderful smells were emanating from the kitchen.

Alexia called to me. "James, the leasing company left dinner and chilled champagne for us. It'll be ready in just a couple of minutes. You'll be joining us."

I was surprised and replied, "Ma'am, I think on your honeymoon …"

Jason laughed and said, "Alexia informed me that it would be better if I didn't think and simply did what she said. At least for tonight, that may go for you, too."

I nodded humbly said, "Yes, sir. That may be best."

Alexia came into the great room carrying a tray with champagne and glasses. She set the tray on the coffee table and said, "Dinner will be in five minutes. I thought we'd have a glass of champagne first."

Jason poured, and we each took a glass.

The newlyweds both looked at each other and then turned toward me.

I said, "If I may propose a toast."

I thought for a minute, cleared my throat, and proclaimed, "To the gift of life's Ultimate Journey."

We clinked glasses and drank.

The dinner and conversation were wonderful, and as the meal was winding down, I spoke up. "Jason and Alexia, before I depart, I have a wedding present that I would like to leave with you."

I deflected all their questions and led them back into the great room. I sat the wrapped package on the coffee table and said, "Before you open it, I think Mr. Stevens' final message from The Ultimate Gift might set the stage appropriately."

I put the DVD that Mr. Hamilton had given me for this occasion into the player. Red Stevens, once again, appeared on the screen to deliver the final message he had given to his grandson.

"Well, if you're standing here now that means that not only have you succeeded in receiving all my gifts, but you've done so beyond the boundaries that I've set. I guess that means that I have succeeded as well. What I could not accomplish in life I've done in death. As long as you are still alive, I will be too.

"I love you, son.

"Good-bye, Jason."

As the screen faded to black, I handed Jason and Alexia their package. As they tore the wrapping paper away, they saw the two brand-new diaries that I had purchased for them.

I spoke what I felt in my heart. "May you live long and well. And may your love grow every day. Fill those pages with words that speak of a life worthy of where you came from, who you are, and what you can be."

I hugged them both and said my good-byes.

As the last glow of an unforgettable day touched the sky, I settled into my customary place behind the steering wheel of the Stevens limousine.

Old habits die hard, and as I started the engine, I glanced into the mirror, expecting Red Stevens to give me his customary signal to proceed. Although the backseat was empty, I felt his unmistakable presence and could almost hear his familiar words. "James, you know what to do."

As I pulled onto the highway and pointed the limousine toward home, I thought about all that had happened that day.

Life is, indeed, a gift. Often, it takes us on a journey to faraway places to be met with exciting people and transforming experiences. Then, inevitably, our journey leads us back into the familiar place where we started, but we are somehow changed as we go home to a place we've never been before.

About the Author

Jim Stovall is among the most sought-after motivational speakers in the world today. Despite failing eyesight and eventual blindness, he has been a national champion Olympic weightlifter, a successful investment broker, and an entrepreneur. He is the cofounder and president of the Emmy Award–winning Narrative Television Network, which makes movies and television accessible for America's thirteen million blind and visually impaired people and their families.

Jim Stovall joined the ranks of Walt Disney, Orson Welles, and four US presidents when he was selected as one of the Ten Outstanding Young Americans. The President's Committee on Equal Employment Opportunity honored him as the Entrepreneur of the Year in a ceremony at the US Capitol. He has appeared on *Good Morning America* and CNN, and has been featured in *Reader's Digest*, *TV Guide*, and *Time* magazine. In June 2000, Jim Stovall joined President Jimmy Carter, Nancy Reagan, and Mother Teresa when he was selected as the International Humanitarian.

He is the author of fifteen books, including the two previous titles in this series, the best-selling *The Ultimate Gift* and *The Ultimate Life*, both of which have been made into major motion pictures by 20th Century Fox.

Jim can be reached at 918-627-1000 or Jim@JimStovall.com.

**The Ultimate Gift
Jim Stovall**

978-81-88452-04-0

**The Ultimate Life
Jim Stovall**

978-81-88452-74-3

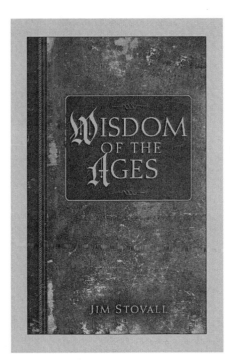

Wisdom Of The Ages
Jim Stovall

978-81-88452-60-6

The Lamp
Jim Stovall

978-93-80227-29-0

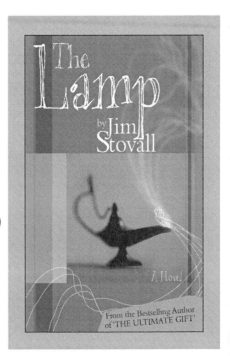